Dementia

hope on a difficult journey

Published by Redemptorist Publications

Alphonsus House, Chawton, Hampshire, GU34 3HQ, UK
Tel. +44 (0)1420 88222, Fax. +44 (0)1420 88805
Email rp@rpbooks.co.uk, www.rpbooks.co.uk

A registered charity limited by guarantee
Registered in England 3261721

First published November 2016
Reprinted April 2018

Text by Dr Adrian Treloar
Edited by Mandy Woods
Designed by Christine Reissland & Eliana Thompson

ISBN 978-0-85231-471-5

A CIP catalogue record for this book is available from the British Library.

The publisher gratefully acknowledges permission to use the following copyright material:

Excerpts from The Jerusalem Bible, copyright © 1966 by Darton, Longman & Todd, Ltd and Doubleday, a division of Random House, Inc. Reprinted by permission.

Images: p.8: Celeste Treloar; p.98: 'Resurrection' by John Warden, courtesy of Adrian Treloar.

Printed by Lithgo Press Ltd.,
Leicester LE8 6NU

Dementia

hope on a difficult journey

Dr Adrian Treloar

Practical and spiritual care of dementia

About the author

I have been a consultant and senior lecturer in old-age psychiatry since 1995. I have developed and run services for people with all stages and severities of dementia. I am also a Catholic. Therefore what I say is in a significant way said from that perspective. But the reality of what I say is very much applicable to those of all faiths.

The primary aim of this book is to help people of the Catholic faith as they seek to provide practical and spiritual care for those with dementia. But I also hope that it may show the way for those of other faiths to help people with dementia. Each faith should bring its own structure to the spiritual needs of its people with dementia.

The greatest sadness is if professionals feel that they are unable or not allowed to help and support the spiritual needs of all the patients for whom they care. Accepting that situation would be a very real surrender to the modern and aggressive march of atheistic secularism. Worse still, if we do not provide spiritual and faith-based support to those who are sick and dying, we deny them their fundamental rights to be respected and supported in their beliefs.

Many people with dementia whom we care for carry with them a strong Christian foundation, and I hope that this book will give some ideas as to how those spiritual needs can and should be met. Legal frameworks require that we act in the best interest of those who lack mental capacity, and therefore there is at least some duty upon all professionals (of all faiths and none) to support appropriate spiritual care.

I hope very much therefore that this little book may help people to understand more about dementia and to feel a little more confident as they set off to accompany a loved one on their journey through dementia. There is much to hope for and much that good care can achieve.

For those who are not Christian

I hope that as they thumb through this book, people of other faiths as well as those of no faith will be able to reflect upon some of the needs and aspirations of people of Christian faith, as well as the true purposes of the care we all offer. The Catholic Church has been central to the development of medical ethics. Christianity was central to the creation of the very health and social care systems that we know today.

Acknowledgements

I am hugely grateful to my family – my long-suffering children and wife – who have helped me as I write this book. I am also grateful to all those patients and their family members who have taught me so much as we have journeyed together through their illnesses. Being a specialist in dementia care is, in the end, a real privilege.

Contents

Introduction

Being ill and having dementia

For all of us, at all ages, illness is a time when things are different. Often enough, illness is also a time when we are bound to reflect – to think more about why we are here and where we are going. Illness is an important time, when support is needed from doctors and nurses, but also from our friends, carers and members of our wider community. As we think about where we are going, illness is also a time when we need help and support from our Church or other faith communities.

If you ask a hundred people in an audience (or ask yourself) if they would like to live long enough to get dementia, almost all will say no. If you ask the same people if they would like to live long enough to see and provide care and support for their grandchildren, almost all will say yes. Most people will also see the puzzling conflict between the first choice and the second choice. People don't want to get dementia but they do want to live long enough to see their children grow up. In fact, some people get dementia before the age of ten. So anyone reading this book will already be older than someone else who has dementia.

More importantly, while no one wants to get dementia, people often forget that people with dementia can contribute enormously to friends and family around them and can also live well. Many people with dementia are happy, and some are even happier than they were before they got it. Imagine a world when you no longer need to run the home, run a business, or sit at the checkout for eight hours each day. With the right care and the right comfort, some people forget the things they have worried about for years and can move on from the difficulties that have beset them for much of their life.

But others suffer. Some suffer very greatly. Depression, hallucinations and paranoia are common in dementia, and pain is often undertreated. It is also easier to miss infection and other illnesses in dementia. People who are confused do not complain as effectively as those who are not confused. Some people with dementia who are distressed find themselves sedated without being given the effective treatment for the cause of their distress.

Good health and social care services are central components of good care, but alongside those services, many others have a crucial role in supporting people and alleviating suffering as people journey through a dementia illness.

Throughout all of that journey, there is a real need for both practical and spiritual support. It is a fundamental article of the Christian faith that prayer makes a difference and is effective. That difference is thought of by many as making people feel comforted or happier, making them feel supported and valued. A feel-good effect. But we also believe (and see good evidence) that prayer brings divine support and enables real change through the graces received. Prayers work, not only as a psychological support, but also as a means of obtaining God's help in a difficult place.

Spiritual care is therefore a really important component of good dementia care. It needs to be available and needs to be offered. Indeed, health care workers should be expected to enable access to it, especially for those who are too confused to request it for themselves. I shall describe later some of its really positive effects.

Some people with dementia and many of those who care for people with dementia feel abandoned by God at a difficult time. In fact we can be sure that God cares enormously about those who suffer dementia. But God is so humble that he relies upon those who care to show his love and the way towards his kingdom. The reward of that kingdom doubtless outweighs any suffering on this earth. But in the middle of a difficult journey through dementia, few will be able to see that.

In this book, I will talk a bit about what dementia is, and follow that with some advice on good care and communication and the management of distress. In the second part of the book, we will look at key aspects of spiritual care, and will include some thoughts on how we can provide that spiritual care.

God is so humble that he relies upon those who care to show his love and the way towards his kingdom.

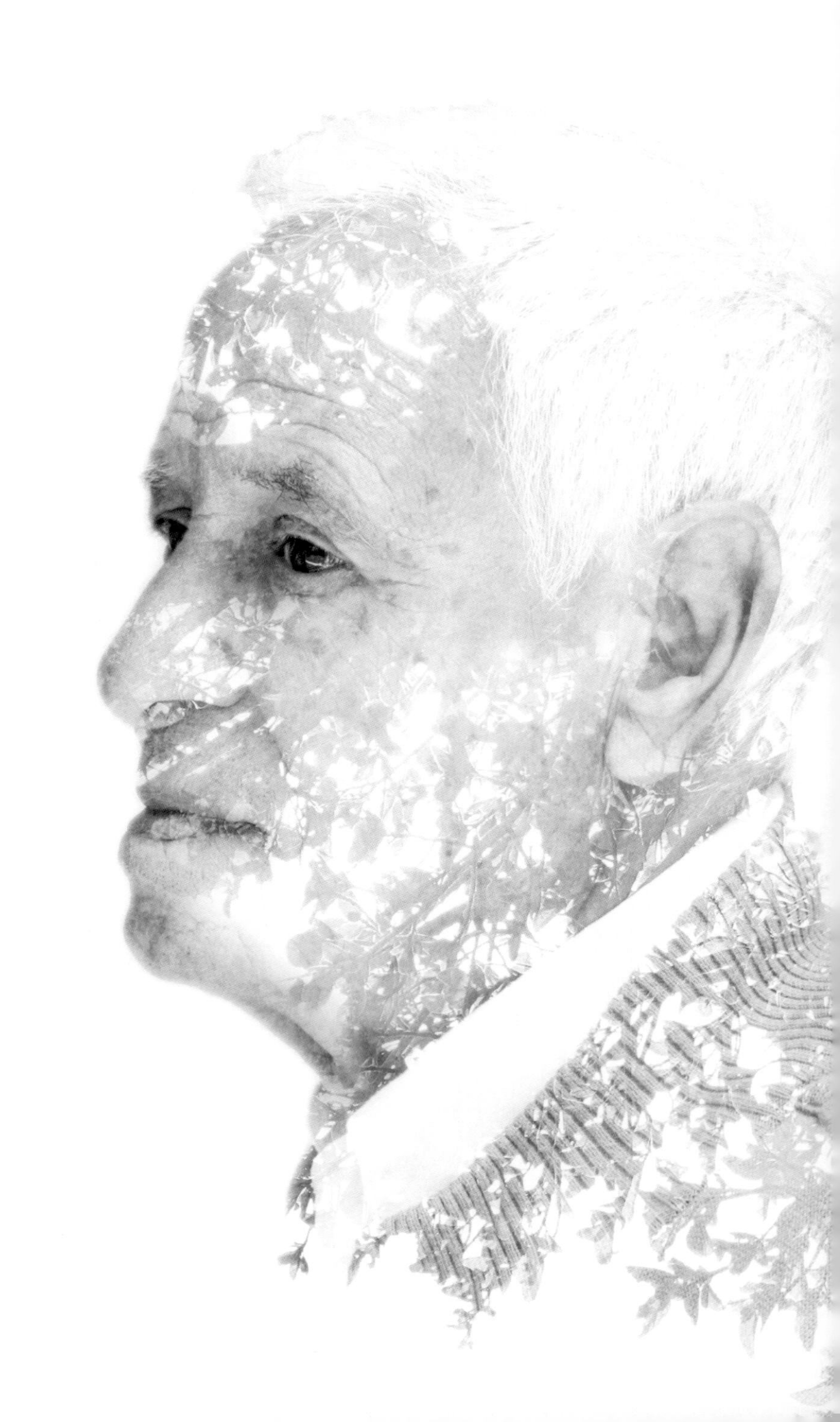

~ Chapter One ~

What is dementia?

Dementia is an illness of the brain. A range of diseases and conditions cause brain cells to die, and as a result of that, the connections between cells are lost. Connections are what make the brain work and what enable us to think. As a result of their loss, the entire brain functions less well. As well as difficulties with memory, there are changes in personality, a reduced ability to do things, reduced understanding and a reduced ability to communicate. Looked at on a brain scan, the most obvious change is often that the amount of brain has reduced.

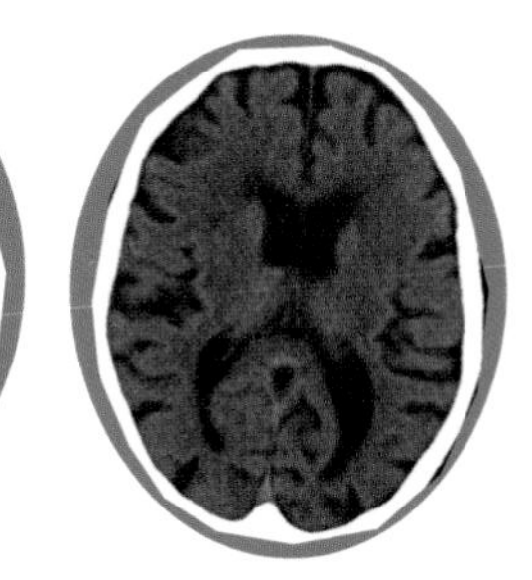

Brain scans showing changes typical in dementia (right) compared with a healthy brain (left)

Dementia is also a progressive condition. With a few exceptions, once the illness has started it will progress and get worse. There are different underlying causes of dementia. The two most common forms are Alzheimer's dementia and vascular dementia. In all forms of dementia a loss of brain cells is the fundamental problem. Some brain cells are very small, and others are very long. The longest cells go all the way from your head to your toes. To stay alive, those cells must be protected and supported by other cells around them, and they also have to be able to transport proteins and other nutrients all the way along their length. Doing that requires some very long "tubules" inside the cells.

These act a bit like tramlines to carry things up and down the cells. A protein called Tau helps the tramlines stay straight.

In Alzheimer's dementia, Tau collapses into twisted strands called tangles. The tubules can no longer stay straight and they fall apart and disintegrate. Because of that, nutrients and other essential supplies can no longer move through the cells, which then die, leaving deposits of dead cells called plaques. Looked at down a microscope, those cells contain the "plaques and tangles" which are characteristic of a brain with Alzheimer's dementia.

In vascular dementia, the small blood vessels in the brain become diseased and many small islands of brain tissue are killed by the shortage of blood. Put together, all of those little islands of dead cells lead to a vascular dementia.

In terms of the symptoms and signs that each person presents, there is not much difference between the Alzheimer's and vascular types of dementia. In fact, probably the largest group of people with dementia have a combination of vascular and Alzheimer's types of dementia.

As well as these two most common forms of dementia, there are others too. Dementia with Lewy bodies (DLB) is a form of dementia related to Parkinson's disease and may result in particularly strong hallucinations, delusions and fear. DLBs also often fluctuate.

"Fronto-temporal" dementias often affect somewhat younger people than other forms of dementia. People with fronto-temporal dementias may retain quite good memory, but you do see changes in personality, disinhibition and other behaviours (sometimes including criminal behaviours). Those complex behaviours can be really quite difficult to manage.

Because dementia is an illness of the brain, it brings with it the need for real changes in the way we live. Life is truly (and often radically) changed. It is very definitely not enough just to be nice, caring and comforting to people with dementia. As well as that, we have to understand that the difficulties and the behaviours that we see are fundamentally caused by that illness. As such, the distress and behaviours are to be seen as expressions of that illness. In people with dementia who swear, or who are aggressive or even sexually disinhibited, we see signs of an illness. In dementia, the illness itself makes the brain do things differently and we do not (and should not) think of behaviours as bad or sinful. They reflect the illness, and not the person. However bad they may appear, those behaviours are in fact signs of disability. Sometimes a person with dementia may be ghastly to their spouse and family. It helps to remember that this is illness, and it does not reflect the way that person would have wanted to behave when they were well and younger. The emotional attacks and insults may still be very hard to bear, and the person with dementia may well retain the ability to make those attacks as effective as possible, but recognising that this is the illness and not the person can be a great help. This mindset can help to lessen the impact on carers of the sufferer's irrational behaviour and hurtful comments.

Recognising that difficult behaviour is the illness and not the person can be a great help.

But as well as that, given that dementia is an illness, being kind and caring is essential but not enough. Treatments are also needed to alleviate the symptoms and distress of what is a major brain illness. At least in part, we have to respond to dementia with treatments and care, in the same way that we would respond to any other physical illness.

~ Chapter Two ~

The opportunity to care for the other

Perhaps one of the greatest difficulties faced by people with dementia is the struggle to remember what to do, and to understand how to do things. It is probably true that by far the most powerful treatment we can offer people with dementia is *somebody*, such as a care worker or a friend, coming in regularly, to provide care, support and real practical help.

Doris was struggling at home. The heating was not working and the boiler was making a dreadful noise. The house was cold and damp, the kitchen was untidy, and the fridge had a little mouldy food left in it. Doris was hungry and had struggled alone for a while until found by her district nurse on a routine check. She had actually also become paranoid, believing that people had broken the heating and were trying to get her out of the house by making all that noise.

Following a good clean-up of the house, the heating was fixed and someone started going in regularly to provide hot meals and food and ongoing support, and Doris was at last warm, less hungry and supplied with regular company. Sometimes the most powerful treatments we can give are kindness and social support.

Churches are often well placed to deliver that care and support and do indeed provide a substantial proportion of such care in the UK.

Providing good care can make a huge difference to someone living with dementia. From a position of loneliness and living in an unclean and cold home, changes can enable them to enjoy comfort once again, and great dignity can be restored. The care workers who achieve that are often quite extraordinary, hard-working, humble and good people.

The most powerful treatment we can offer people with dementia is *somebody*, such as a care worker or a friend, coming in regularly to provide care, support and real practical help.

"Looking after Grace was never hard work, it was like a person who converts a piece of scrubland into a beautiful garden – he may work very hard, but when he sees the results of his labours he never thinks about how much time and hard work he put into it. His efforts were well worthwhile. Frankly, I would do the same thing over again, except I would, with the experience I have gained, do a much better job."

Jack

It has been said that societies can be judged by the care and concern that they show towards their most vulnerable members. In dementia, we can see a unique opportunity for the healthy to provide care for the sick. We normally think that the provision of care is something that we (the healthy) do for them (the sick). But in fact what is really intriguing is that we are ourselves dignified by the care that we offer to the sick. By accepting care and support, people with dementia can give a great deal to those who care for them.

A good example of this might be the husband who just wants to pay back some of the goodness his wife showed him when she was younger and healthy. People who have cared for loved ones with dementia may well be exhausted and worn out by doing so. But some recognise how much it all means and how special it is for them to be able to care. And, arguably, almost all are dignified by the care they show to their loved ones.

Providing care can be massively challenging and stressful, but it can also be very rewarding. One lesson from cancer care is that when it is possible for family members to carry on providing care right through to the end, bereavement reactions may be less severe than when the family is not able to give that care.

But we should note here that for some, the work of caring is too much. There are many reasons why this may be so, including frailty in the carer, responsibility for others, including children, lack of space and other difficulties. When it is all too much, it is right for them to allow others to provide care while they stand back.

~ Chapter Three ~

Hope, trust and fear of the unknown

Nobody will relish the prospect of getting dementia. Some may make light of it, mindful of the fact that people with dementia have fewer responsibilities, and can in fact behave in ways that would never have been acceptable when they were well. But, rightly, dementia is something which is feared and unwanted.

Many people just fear getting ill. Others fear greatly the loss of dignity that they see following on from incontinence and dependence. Some fear losing their intellectual abilities and more just cannot bear to think about the future.

> So do not worry about tomorrow, for tomorrow will bring worries of its own. Today's trouble is enough for today.
>
> MATTHEW 6:34

The unknown will always be a difficult thing to plan for and something that people will worry about a lot. Building on the Gospel of St Matthew, St Thomas à Kempis tells us: "Sorrow upon sorrow can be the only result if you worry about the future. Sufficient to the day is the evil in it. It is quite vain and useless to be either anxious or pleased about the future, for what you anticipate may never happen." St Thomas describes well the ways in which fear of the future can indeed make today worse. Sometimes planning for the future can be helpful and feel reassuring, but other times such planning can be harmful.

Most of all, we need to be able to hope that good care will be provided, and that does require a degree of trust. Trust in our family and friends, and also trust in others. The reality is that the world is full of a huge number of good people and few bad ones. While taking patients with dementia out to help them walk off their agitation and distress, I have found that people will stop and ask if we are okay or whether we need help. Many are willing to offer assistance; only a few are malign.

> "At times when I took my mum out, she would refuse to get into the car to come home and I always found members of the public very helpful in encouraging her that everything was alright. Most times they would tell me that they also had a relative with dementia and they understood. Carers should not be afraid to ask for help from others."

I was once cross-examined in court during the trial of a man accused of taking money from his mother. The defence lawyer asked me the following question: "So would you say, Doctor, that in dementia you go from ability to loss of dignity?" My answer was a resounding "NO". Both he and I had the full ability to go out any night and get drunk and act in a deeply undignified way. But I have seen the greatest dignity in people with a very advanced dementia at the very end of their lives.

Dignity does not have to be lost when you develop a severe dementia. The most wonderful dignity can be afforded by providing good care to our most disabled and vulnerable citizens.

> "We hear mostly about the negative changes in behaviour of the dementia sufferer. My mum became sweeter, kinder, more compassionate and loving as her illness progressed. It was as though she was being polished like a diamond. She was always grateful and constantly thanking everyone for any kindness shown her."

Dignity does not have to be lost when you develop a severe dementia

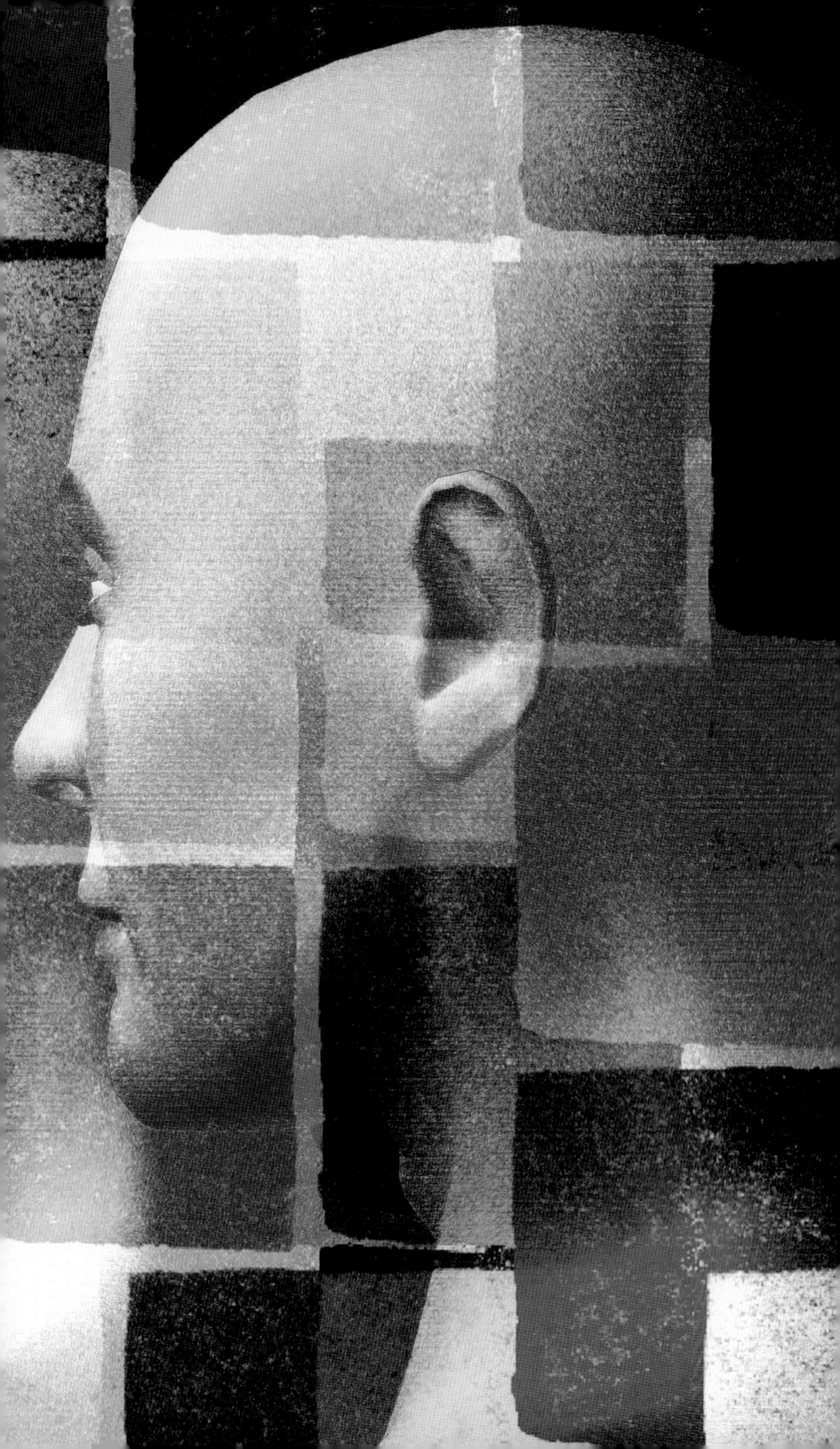

~ Chapter Four ~

Medical treatments for dementia

Treatments that delay the progression of dementia

At the present time there are no treatments that slow the progression of the Alzheimer's type of dementia. But there is great hope that by 2025 there may be some treatments.

With vascular dementia (caused by blood vessel disease in the brain), it is possible that treatment with blood-thinning and blood-pressure medicines as well as cholesterol-lowering medicines may make a difference and slow progression, preserving health for at least a little longer.

With some rarer sorts of dementia, such as AIDS-related dementia, treatment can dramatically alter the progress of the disease.

Treatments that improve memory

One thing that we can do is offer drugs that may improve memory. These drugs usually have a small effect and do not help everyone. Typically about a third of people improve, a third stop deteriorating for a while and the others show no effect from the medicine at all. While the effect is only small and definitely not a cure, both patients and carers are often very positive about the benefits. For a few, some skills may return. For others, carers may describe the person with dementia as being "more with it". And in terms of overall effect, the benefits appear to delay the severity of symptoms and the increasing need for care for between six months and a year. That may well mean a year longer at home living independently. And patients and carers enormously value that extra time and ability.

In the past, these medicines used to be stopped once the dementia had progressed somewhat, but nowadays many are able to continue the drugs with some benefit right on into the advanced stages of the illness.

Many people live well with dementia, and some are in fact happier once they are affected by it than they were before. But others suffer greatly with it. Distress is therefore a very important problem in dementia. Some treatments of dementia rightly focus upon its distressing symptoms. Medical treatments such as pain-killing medicines, antidepressants and antipsychotics all have their place in managing the distress experienced by some people with dementia. This will be discussed in more detail in Chapter 13. But as well as medical treatments for dementia, there are a whole range of other ways in which we can dramatically improve the experience of dementia.

Treatments that help with other symptoms

For those who live well with dementia and do not appear to suffer, we should just perhaps carry on, hoping that with the right support and care, this will be enough. And not everything needs to be treated. For example, people often have hallucinations that are not distressing. These do not need to be taken away with medication. Relatives may be worried about such symptoms, and may need reassuring that as long as their loved one is not distressed by them, they do not (usually) need treatment.

But for those who do suffer, and especially those who suffer greatly, we should focus upon treating and alleviating that suffering.

Depression and psychosis (seeing things or believing dreadful things may be happening) are common in people with dementia. The majority will show evidence of depression at some time in the illness and psychosis also occurs in most sufferers. It is important to treat both of these if they occur. Although the evidence base for effectiveness is limited, we know that people respond to treatment for both and that they may deteriorate if treatment is stopped.

It may be right and good to treat a person who is suffering from hallucinations or severe fear with antipsychotic medicines even though those drugs can be harmful. It is wrong to leave a person with severe dementia to suffer.

There are harmful side effects, especially as a result of anti-psychotic medicines which increase the risk of strokes, falls, worsened confusion and death. But if someone is really suffering from a psychosis and treatment can alleviate that suffering, it is right (and Church teaching is also clear that it is right) to treat that person with an effective medicine even though there is risk of serious harm. Happily the frequency of strokes, death and other harmful side effects is still low, with the large majority not suffering from them at all. Once a person has settled down again, a cautious withdrawal of medicines may be tried, although many carers and spouses are reluctant to see the medicines stopped because they fear a relapse when their loved one is not taking the medication.

Remember to think of pain as a possibility in people with dementia. It is easily missed and can cause a lot of distress to such people.

Antidepressants are probably harmless enough to just continue with for ever if someone is thought to have benefited from them.

Pain is a very important issue in dementia. We know that people with dementia get fewer painkillers than their healthy counterparts, and yet we think they experience pain as much or more. It seems that doctors and nurses forget to give pain relief like they do for healthier people.

And infections make all sorts of things worse, including confusion, and need to be watched for carefully.

> "Mum's confusion would become more intense when she had a urinary tract infection and her increased confusion became an indicator of this."

Make a life-story book with a family member. It's a nice project to do in early dementia. Later on, this can be used to help others understand the person with dementia better. And you can sit and thumb through it together.

~ Chapter Five ~

Planning and thinking about the future

Making some plans for the future is a good and sensible idea. If someone becomes unable to manage their own finances and affairs, legal instruments can be drawn up to allow someone else to do these things on their behalf. In England and Wales that is called a Lasting Power of Attorney for property and finance. Once it is enacted, the person or people you appoint will have full powers to spend your money and also to sell your house and other property. So you do need to be sure that you can trust the people you appoint. Sometimes it is better to appoint two or three people so that they can keep an eye on each other. Doing so may mean that children are less likely to worry about what one another is doing.

Lasting Powers of Attorney in England and Wales can enable real and practical help at the right time. And they also allow the person with dementia to choose (early on) who they trust to support them later on.

> The Power of Attorney can be very important and needs to be obtained while the dementia sufferer is of sound enough mind to grant it. Unfortunately, the dementia is often too far progressed by the time this is realised.

You can also sign a Lasting Power of Attorney for health and welfare, which gives the person whom you appoint the power to consent to and refuse health care on your behalf. It also requires doctors and nurses and other medical professionals to consult with the appointed person about decisions that normally need consent.

There can be problems with all of these legal tools. Of course, especially, with money – if the person you appoint acts badly or takes your money for themselves, they can be imprisoned. Such corruption is not as rare as we would hope. It is always worth keeping an eye out for things that seem wrong. But generally, Lasting Powers of Attorney can be very helpful and effective. They can be set up at any age, long before the first suspicion of dementia. They are well worth thinking about once a diagnosis is made. If you leave it too late after a diagnosis, you will not be able to appoint anyone.

Benefits and problems with advance care planning

In Britain and in many other countries it is possible to write documents that describe the sort of health care you wish to refuse when you have become unwell. Broad statements that we recognise our mortality and that when we are ill we would not want very burdensome treatments can be helpful to doctors and nurses at some time in the future. It may also be helpful to state that you accept that in advanced disease, comfort and the alleviation of distress may be a sensible priority over and above curative medicine and treatments that will not work.

> There are risks that advance decisions to refuse treatment may have unintended consequences and might cause prolonged suffering.

But precise refusals can also risk significant unintended harm. For example, while some statements about future health care wishes can be helpful, many have been tempted to write statements such as: "If I have severe dementia I only want treatments that alleviate pain and refuse any active, curative treatments." That may sound good, but in fact, if once you have developed a severe dementia you break your hip or get a urine infection, the effective treatment of the pain and disability is surgery (for the hip) or an antibiotic (for the infection). Non-treatment probably does not cause death, but will cause significant suffering and probably substantially worse confusion. Some caution is therefore needed in writing advance refusals, and it is wise to avoid being too specific about future situations which you cannot accurately predict and where a decision made now might lead to real difficulties for you.

Alternatives such as Lasting Powers of Attorney (see above) may work better and can be more flexible, enabling decisions to be made at the time which are crafted to whatever situation has developed.

The situation concerning priests, religious and people with no next of kin

When such people become ill, the hospital may well need someone to talk to, to advise on their wishes, preferences and good care. But hospitals do not always recognise the bishop, superior or brothers as the next of kin (thinking of them more as "managers"). If you have no next of kin, do write something down, witnessed, stating who you wish to act as a decision-maker. This would best be done as a Lasting Power of Attorney for Health and Welfare. Otherwise, you may find that (on grounds of confidentiality) the hospital refuses to tell members of your order what is going on and being done for you.

~ Chapter Six ~

Security of person

One of the most basic human rights is a person's right to liberty and security. As people develop dementia, it is often both right and necessary that, to some degree, liberty may necessarily become compromised. As you become more forgetful and more unable, it is right and proper that you may need to be supervised if you are going out. Allowing an old person to go out late at night and get lost on the local buses would clearly constitute neglect and may be harmful or lethal. It is always a good idea to try and support people in continuing to go to the places they always did (e.g. church, the shops, visiting family), but it is also necessary to protect people, to give them security of person.

That security is a basic right and can be provided in a number of ways. First, just being there, supporting and accompanying the person with dementia, makes a huge difference. Confused people who are supported to shop, cook and get dressed can achieve this for far longer with help than they can on their own.

For people with more severe dementia, it may become necessary to ensure that someone is around to remind them to do things, to provide warm food and snacks, to encourage them to drink, and to remind them to take medicines and to go to the toilet.

> Churches are well placed to provide care and security to people who are in need and at risk.

And with even more severe dementia, it is necessary to make sure people do some things and do not do others. It may be necessary and right, for example, to have a locked door to make sure they do not wander out and come to harm. It may also be right to make sure they are toileted or changed. And it is right to be sure that they have enough clothes to be warm, etc. All of these become duties of care to ensure the security of that person. With that security there can be great comfort and dignity, while without it, neglect and great suffering may occur.

But there are times when society's focus on autonomy and choice distracts people away from good care, compassion and providing security of person. Indeed, the societal focus on autonomy and choice really does not work all that well for people who are severely confused and cannot understand what they are choosing. Compassion, caring and a very deep respect for the individual who needs help become very important when we have to impose care.

Compassion, caring and a very deep respect for the individual who needs help become very important when we have to impose care.

There are times when care does have to be imposed. Especially when that care requires significant supervision and control over an individual, there may be a need for legal safeguards to ensure that it is done sensibly and properly. In England and Wales the Mental Capacity Act regulates the way in which we can provide care to people who are confused and lack "mental capacity". But those laws must be used to enable what is needed to provide security of person. That security of person is a fundamental plank of the Human Rights Act. And protection of the vulnerable is a central duty of compassionate humanity.

The place of the Church and the laity in providing security to those at risk

Churches are well placed to provide care and security to people who are in need and at risk. Partly by bringing the sacraments to the sick, and partly just through their work in supporting those in need, the churches (both priests and laity) have a central role in supporting people with dementia. Churches should always be aware of the possible need for help when they find that parishioners are forgetting things, turning up late for Mass, or just looking more tired or less well cared for.

For a while the best solution may well combine things such as help with shopping and making sure that someone is brought to Mass regularly. In that way, the person with dementia can carry on being out and about and stay in communion with the other members of the church. But later on, taking the sacraments to them and taking care to them becomes the right way forward. The balance here is an attempt to keep people doing the things they always did while not taking over their activities and duties until that is necessary.

As Christians, we should apply the highest standards, and there is an expectation that we will deliver high-quality care honestly and compassionately. And as Christians, we should also be absolutely intolerant of any dishonesty towards, or abuse of, people with dementia and other vulnerable people. Any concerns should be reported so that they can be investigated. Each parish will have its own identified coordinator for safeguarding children and vulnerable people.

But churches comprise a vast resource of good-minded people who in fact do deliver very large amounts of voluntary care, supporting and visiting the sick. This is a tradition that the churches should be proud of, while carefully continuing to ensure that the care is delivered well and effectively. In addition, many churches will have doctors, nurses, social workers and others in their congregations who can advise and support those who are providing the front-line care and support. The tradition of supporting the needy stretches right back to St Stephen (the first martyr) and is a very real part of the mission of all Christian Churches in the world today.

As Christians, we should also be absolutely intolerant of any dishonesty towards, or abuse of, people with dementia and other vulnerable people. Any concerns should be reported so that they can be investigated.

Imposing care in difficult circumstances

Most care can be delivered with the agreement of an individual with dementia and by working with them. If something is refused at first, it may well be accepted later. Making light of things may help, and there are many other ways in which it is possible to help people with dementia to agree to care which is necessary.

But however well meaning we are, and however well we do things, there will be times when care has to be imposed upon people with dementia. Some, for example, simply cannot be persuaded to stay at home, insisting that they go out at night and in freezing weather. Others refuse to be washed or dressed. Others may become very scared and as a result be aggressive to others, hitting out and risking injury.

In such circumstances, care may still be deliverable in different ways, and by skilled people, or by people who just happen to get it right at the crucial moment. Just waiting and trying again an hour later may be all that is needed.

But at other times, care will have to be imposed. People with dementia may need to be stopped from going out. Doors may need to be locked. Pants and pads may need to be changed, and in the end, to prevent serious harm from the development of infections and sores, it may be necessary to ensure that someone is "cleaned up". Medicines too may need to be imposed in the face of resistance.

In all these circumstances the reason for providing care is to avoid harm coming to the individual and because they are not able to understand why they need help or care. It is not only right to impose care in such circumstances; failure to do so may constitute serious neglect. As already stated, we should be intolerant of abuse, and neglect can be a very serious form of abuse.

So if you think someone is suffering or neglected or requires care, it is worth asking a few questions.

- Does the person understand why they need care?
- Is it possible to explain this to them and to help them understand and agree to care?
- If they cannot understand (that is, if they lack the mental capacity to make a decision), what is it that needs to be done and how might it be done?
- Is it possible to delay doing it or to do it in a way that is less imposing?
- Have you thought about and (if there is time) spoken to family members, carers or next of kin?
- Is it urgently necessary to act to preserve the person's health?

Having answered all of those questions, you will hopefully feel that you can justify your actions and then proceed to provide the necessary care, in the "least restrictive way". That term "least restrictive" is a legal term which is enshrined in the Mental Capacity Act, and it means that we should try always to find a less imposing way of doing things if possible. But remember, neglect is wrong, and worries about imposing care should not mean that people with dementia suffer neglect or are harmed as a result of neglect.

There are several legal structures that can be used to enable the imposition of care. In England and Wales the Mental Capacity Act and Deprivation of Liberty Safeguards are the most commonly used. Those laws enable the legal imposition of care.

> Neglect is wrong, and worries about imposing care should not mean that people with dementia suffer neglect or are harmed as a result of neglect.

Protection of the vulnerable is a central duty of compassionate care. That means that those imposing care should be sure to act within the law.

Imposing routine care

Some people think that the only type of care that we can impose is urgent or life-saving care. Actually, we can (and should) also impose routine care if that care is necessary to provide comfort, avoid harm or just keep someone well. For example, simply changing someone so that they are clean and avoid sores, or treating a urine infection or high blood pressure, may well avert serious harm even though the care needed is only routine. Therefore it is right and proper to impose the care that the person with dementia needs for their comfort and security. Depriving someone of their liberty is sometimes a necessary and essential part of good care. By depriving someone of their liberty we provide them with a fundamental human right: security of person.

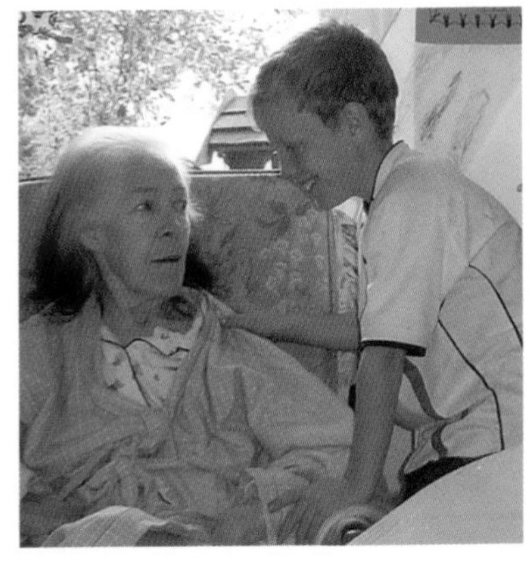

The greatest need in dementia is for really good care. Without care, people will suffer in pain or distress and discomfort. Support is so much more effective than any other medication or treatment. Sensitive support, coupled with understanding, good communication, respect and love, is absolutely essential. With it, the need for imposition of care will normally be reduced and may even be eliminated.

~ Chapter Seven ~

Ways of communicating

Communication is a really important issue in dementia care. Anyone visiting someone with dementia needs to take time and they need to be relaxed. Don't make things too complicated. It is a real blessing to be able to enjoy the person you are with. If you know more about their background, this becomes easier. It makes it possible to do things differently, and people with dementia usually remember the past much better than they remember the present. In this context, discussion about the past may well be helpful.

> "One of the most challenging aspects of my mum's dementia was the way – in a conversation – she would come and go mentally within sentences. I would feel that I was connecting with her and she would suddenly be whisked away again. This was difficult to get the hang of and cope with."

A gentle chat about church last Sunday will remind the individual of their trips to church throughout their life. Equally, gentle chats about anything relatively trivial will give a calm and relaxing atmosphere, enabling the best communication and the best quality of interaction.

People with dementia become distressed when they cannot understand. They equally become distressed when they cannot work out how to reply to somebody. So it's really important to try and avoid arguments. It's also useful to try and put the answers into questions.

Rather than saying, "Hello, how are you? Do you want Holy Communion?" it is perhaps a little better to try something like: "Hello Pat. I'm Anne from church. It's my day for visiting you and so I brought you Holy Communion. Is that OK?" The latter may well get a far more positive response. The point is to help the person with dementia to feel more confident and to familiarise them with what is happening so that they may feel more relaxed and more able to accept help or care.

Remember the use of touch. If in the past you held hands or put your hand on their shoulder, it may be comforting and reassuring to do this now with the person with dementia. Remember, however, that touching is not always appropriate.

Communication is harder for many older people. It is even harder if dentures fit poorly, if hearing is impaired, if vision is poor or if someone is not comfortable. Remember the use of touch. If in the past you held hands or put your hand on their shoulder, it may be comforting and reassuring to do this now with the person with dementia. Remember, however, that touching is not always appropriate.

Speak clearly but don't shout unnecessarily. It is not nice to be shouted at just because you are old. Sit close, show interest and use eye contact to keep their attention. If their recent memory is poor, try talking about things in the past: the war, old cars, old jobs, family stories and so on.

Try to orientate people in time and place. Do this by giving clues in what you say:

WRONG: "Hello dear, do you remember me?"

BETTER: "Hello John, it's that old wife of yours come to see you!"

Don't talk down to people. Treat the person as an equal:

WRONG: "I told you that a minute ago."

BETTER: "Oh, did I forget to tell you that?"

WRONG: "You just told me that, Dad."

BETTER: "Yes, that's right Dad" (i.e. don't draw attention to the fact that he's repeated himself, but agree with him and then simply move on to a new topic).

If there are more than two people present, make sure you include the person with dementia in the conversation:

Visitor: "How is your father today?"

WRONG: "He's not as good as last week." (If you say that, then Dad can't join in.)

BETTER: "Are you a bit less good than last week, Dad?"

To which Dad will probably reply something like:

"Oh I'm not too bad really."

Try to give people with dementia cues and clues as to what is happening or what is needed. Try and get clues to the answers they might give into the questions you ask them, so that they will feel more able to decide what to say and will feel more supported.

Most of all, keep communication simple, talking about familiar and everyday things. Remember that in normal life we talk far more about all the tasks and chores of life. Teatime conversation will often be about cutting the grass, seeing a friend or watching a football match. Mundane things and the things of normal life are the stuff of our conversations. When someone is ill we get distracted into talking about the illness and forgetting everything else. People with dementia enjoy talking about the normal things of life. And while they may be just as proud as ever if their team wins, they can forget their team lost a match more quickly too!

"I would find with my mum that direct questions caused her distress. Her thoughts would become confused as she battled to answer. Gentle, inviting comments, rather than questions, worked better."

In very advanced dementia, people may well lose the ability to understand sentences because they are not able to follow words for the duration of a whole sentence. At such times, making things as simple as possible seems sensible. But remember, when you are ill or struggling a lot, it will often be comforting to have friends around you just chatting, being, and perhaps praying.

Practical tip: sensory loss

Poor hearing and poor eyesight may well contribute to the difficulties experienced by people struggling with dementia. If someone is deaf or has poor eyesight, try and find out what can be done to help. Hearing aids can be very useful, although they are easily lost. Glasses too are easily lost. If cataracts are a problem, they can sometimes be removed, although the soreness of the eye afterwards and remembering not to fiddle with the eye can be a real problem in people with dementia, making surgery significantly more risky.

~ Chapter Eight ~

Memories

Memories can be a powerful way of using yesterday for today's good. With dementia, people are most often better at remembering things from a long time ago. Things that happened today or yesterday fade. There are lots of useful ways of using reminiscence to help gain access to a rich world. It also helps to remember times when the person with dementia was healthy, maybe bringing up a family, and "doing" for others.

Sometimes, the use of memories can be especially powerful in very advanced dementia.

Visiting someone with advanced dementia and limited communication can feel difficult. The following activities will help make it easier:

- Bring a book with pictures to look at together
- Look at old photos or a life-story book
- Listen to music together – sing along
- Watch a nature video together
- Read some poetry together
- Remember rhymes together
- Try praying together

It was Christmas day and Grandma was in bed in the sitting room with the telly on. The Pope came on. "I know him," said Grandma. Despite her very advanced dementia, Grandma still showed real flashes of awareness and the ability to recognise things from years gone by.

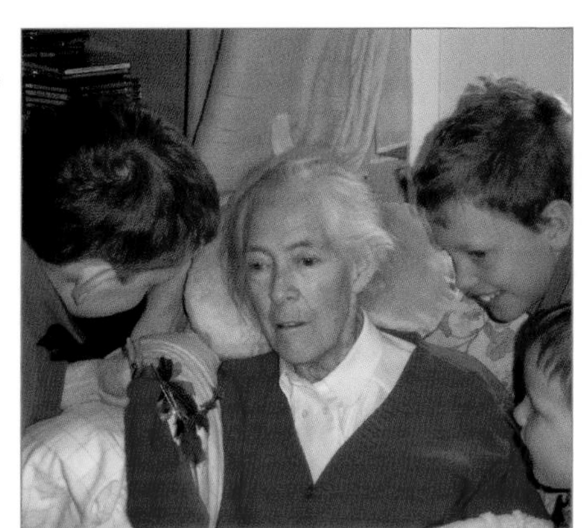

Mum was a WWII veteran and was very proud to march with the veterans to the Cenotaph in London every year in November on Remembrance Day, until the age of eighty-eight when she had her stroke. Thereafter I would put her hat and medal on her on the day and she loved to watch it on TV. The deepest memories seemed to linger, even through the progression of dementia.

~ Chapter Nine ~

Is it enough to be caring and kind? Making changes

Dementia brings the need for real changes as life is truly changed. It is very definitely not enough just to be nice, caring and comforting. Early on, dementia often presents as a subtle set of symptoms when someone is just struggling a bit more than before. Often enough, their struggles will go unnoticed, even though a subtle deterioration is happening in terms of cleanliness at home, food preparation, shopping and cooking, and personal care. At times like this, early on, while some people just do not seem to notice any difficulties, others are especially low in mood and suffering. It is at that earliest stage when we most often see the signs of a stressed or unhappy person.

Even at that early stage, it is really important to think about making some changes. We have already said that one aim of good dementia care is to keep people going for as long as possible in their own homely and familiar setting. But even at that early stage adjustments need to be thought about. The point to remember early on is that small changes can make a big difference and alleviate a lot of worry and distress.

Things to consider early on

- Think about a diagnosis and treatment:
  - Going to a memory clinic may enable a real conversation about having dementia and be of real help
  - Treatment early on may make a difference
- Think about the care and support that may be needed:
  - Help with shopping
  - Help with cleaning and cooking
- Think about someone's safety:
  - Is driving safe?
  - Is the cooker safe?
  - What can be done to make things safer?
- Think about the need for help with money:
  - People with dementia can be very vulnerable to financial abuse, villains and scams

Driving becomes a particular problem as dementia worsens, and the risk of harming others as a result of a car accident may increase. For that reason there are strict laws and regulations relating to driving with dementia. Equally, you cannot legally drive in the UK if you have a diagnosis of dementia and have not told the authorities. We all have a duty to protect both the driver with dementia and the other road users from serious harm. Happily, most people with dementia just give up driving of their own volition. However, there are those whose skills are preserved and who are allowed to carry on driving by the authorities, and we should remember that people with dementia cause substantially less death and destruction on the roads than young teenage and twenty-something males.

You cannot legally drive in the UK if you have a diagnosis of dementia and have not told the authorities.

Later on, as dementia progresses, the need for changes becomes more marked. Some people will be able to carry on living at home for the rest of their lives. That is especially the case when there is a healthy carer (such as a husband, wife, son or daughter) to provide support for them in the home. When that is possible, outcomes can be very good.

At other times, necessary changes will include putting together an extensive care package, modifying the geography of a house, and/or seeking admission to a care home. Old people do have to be flexible – and at times of crisis, they can be amazingly flexible. Younger people might well marvel at how well old people cope with huge changes whose suddenness and scale others may barely comprehend.

Amazing Grace!

Grace, in her seventies, developed a multi-infarct dementia. She became very agitated and went into a nursing home. Within two weeks she had lost weight, was bruised and distressed, and ended up sitting in a basket chair on a dementia assessment ward. She repeatedly called out numbers from ninety-seven to one hundred. It was difficult to see what could be done to alleviate her distress or to care for her. Careful use of antipsychotics and antidepressants had some benefit, and benzodiazepines were used as well. She didn't do that well but settled enough to go into a dementia specialist nursing home. There she lost weight and continued to be distressed, and her husband Jack could not bear to see her in such a way. He asked the doctors for permission to take her home. They were rather reluctant, and thought it a bad idea that was unlikely to work, with a high possibility of death as a result.

They had already told Jack that she was not likely to survive until their fiftieth wedding anniversary. So they all sat and discussed

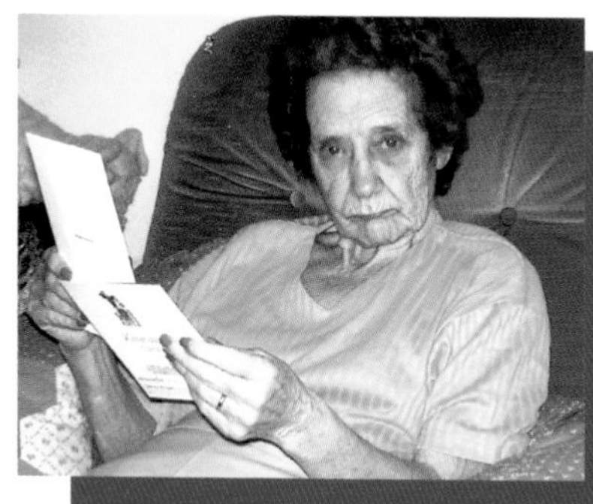

the possibilities. They agreed that whatever happened, Grace should not suffer, but Jack felt that where she was simply was not right. However, it seemed that going home would require a miracle.

The nurses and specialists all said they were very worried about the plan to go home and thought it a bad idea. But Grace's husband insisted, and after discussion it was agreed that this could be tried.

Wonderfully, Grace did well. In fact, she lived at home for eight years and the doctors were able to stop all her psychiatric medicines. Early on, she had needed these very badly, but as her illness progressed, the agitation and distress settled, and all the medicines that were no longer needed were stopped.

Grace gained weight and was happy in the care of her husband, along with a small but loyal group of carers who supported him. For a lady who was fully dependent and needed full nursing care, including feeding, it was extraordinary to see her on trips out to shopping centres and her beloved golf club, amongst other places. She smiled, spoke hardly at all, but watched everything that Jack did. And Jack and Grace proved the doctors wrong: she did live to see their fiftieth wedding anniversary. Grace died quite suddenly one morning after breakfast. She was in bed, and the couple had celebrated their fifty-seventh wedding anniversary.

The doctors think that Grace's long survival was attributable to the good care, along with the fact that this was a multi-infarct dementia and not an Alzheimer's-type dementia. Her dementia stabilised for quite some time and did not progress, explaining the unusually long length of time she was able to survive at home.

As well as taking a real delight in seeing Grace and Jack coping together, the specialists' reaction at the end of this experience was one of genuine pleasure at being proved wrong by them. Jack's brave decision showed that this can be a viable and good way to care for dementia patients.

With permission from <www.hopeforhome.org.uk>.

In addition, being old in general, and having dementia in particular, brings with it the certainty of change which is often sudden and unpredicted. Slips, trips, falls and infections as well as strokes and heart attacks happen more often to people with dementia than to fit and healthy older people. It is in large part these illnesses and sudden deteriorations which account for the shortened life expectancy of people with dementia. But as well as that, the deterioration in self-care and other abilities, slowness to ask for help and general decline are the things which mean that dementia is progressive and causes a dramatic shortening of life expectancy.

It's not enough to make changes once or twice. As we support people through a dementia illness, ongoing change is needed. At particular times of deterioration, changes may be needed even weekly. At other times there may be periods of stability and calm, although care and support will always have to be adjusted and delivered according to need.

> It's not enough to make changes once or twice. As we support people through a dementia illness, ongoing change is needed. At particular times of deterioration, changes may be needed even weekly. At other times there may be periods of stability and calm, although care and support will always have to be adjusted and delivered according to need.

Change is absolutely inevitable on the difficult journey of dementia. That need for change also brings with it the opportunity to think and pray about many things. Of course dementia provides a real prompt to think about our mortality and our salvation. For relatives and carers, it serves as a reminder of the care we owe to our parents, as well as of the vows that we may have taken as spouses before the altar so many years before. And many people do indeed hope that the care they provide for someone with dementia is a testament to their marriage vows and to the great gifts received from the person who now needs their care.

Pat had a severe dementia, but was taken to Mass for the Feast of the Ascension. Mass was in Latin and not everyone was familiar with the "Old Mass". At crucial times during the Mass, Pat knew what to do and led the congregation.

Of course, that somewhat idealistic view of "giving love" is one which inevitably comes apart at the times when we get it wrong. And on the challenging and difficult journey of dementia, we can be pretty sure that at times we will get it wrong. But we will hope that we get it right more often than not. We are challenged to try our best while accepting our frailties and failures. That's not an easy mix!

Finally, when someone with dementia is no longer able to practise their faith by themselves, it is really important that we provide them with the opportunity to continue to do so. By doing so, we are continuing to value and respect them as we should. That will require a range of responses from us, starting off with taking the person to church, then supporting them during Mass, and later on bringing the sacraments to them at home and in hospital.

We are challenged to try our best while accepting our frailties and failures. That's not an easy mix!

As ever, we adjust the way we provide that support according to their changing needs and changing abilities. But we know that God will love to see them there, and others will too. If we leave them alone, we neglect our Christian duty.

Doris lived with her daughter Emily and was taken to Mass each Sunday. Sitting in her wheelchair at the front, she would talk and sing through Mass, at times quite oblivious to what was going on. At other times, she was deeply devout. We missed her so when she was finally gone!

3

~ Chapter Ten ~

Care support

I have already said that perhaps the largest impact upon people with dementia is the support they receive from others. People with dementia become unable to organise themselves and their daily duties, to the point where they struggle and then increasingly fail to manage the basic needs of life.

In dementia, all the things that we normally do, such as washing, dressing, and making food and drinks, become harder. Other tasks, such as shopping, paying bills, and sorting out complex phone calls, become impossible. Bills may go unpaid, kitchens, fridges and toilets uncleaned, and houses unmaintained.

The full range of our daily activities may well, in the end, need support. Care packages need to be built around a person's needs and abilities, and will need to change and develop with time.

People with dementia often mellow and can become enormously more accepting of help and care than they ever were when younger. Just accepting care from others and tolerating being toileted or washed and dressed by their children, or even by a son- or daughter-in-law, are all examples of the way in which people with dementia develop a whole new set of skills with their disability. And in accepting that care, in very many ways they in fact maintain their dignity and are in no way humiliated. At other times, however, care may be resisted and be far from easy to impose (see "Imposing care in difficult circumstances", p. 39).

Progression of care needs

Because dementia is a progressive condition, the need for help will change with time. And therefore the help given must be tailored to individual need over time. While churches and Christians will often focus on spiritual support, they are also ideally placed to be part of the practical caring solution for individual people. It is good to know that churches and their members provide vast quantities of social care and support. The Society of St Vincent de Paul and Eucharistic ministers are all part of this network of care and support.

> Hoists and other equipment such as beds may be essential

Because the response to each individual is individually tailored to their needs, it is not possible to describe a "normal care package". At the early stages, care may start with just a gentle eye being kept on them, and a bit of support with going to clinics and so on. After a while, help with shopping and taking to places such as shops, clubs and church may be needed. Later on that care will progress towards a regular visit to help sort out a hot meal, and onwards towards making sure the person is washed, dressed and kept safe. Medicines may need to be prompted and they may need to be reminded about such things as toileting.

Clearly, with the more personal care, there will be several reasons why such care is most often given by a family member or a paid carer. Older and more frail people may struggle with very practical hands-on care. Intimate care, while absolutely essential, may arouse some concerns if it is done by someone who is not properly regulated and inspected. Having said that, we should not avoid taking risks; while we should be cautious about providing personal care, we should also be cautious about standing back and not helping to provide care that is needed. Rather, we should engage with the challenge and make sure that anything we do can be scrutinised if necessary. Solutions to needs are required, especially when someone is suffering.

This is me: making a patient story

It is very important for the person to be known by those who care for them.

It is a good idea for families and carers to write down a history of the person who has dementia. People with dementia often struggle to say what their preferences are, such as:

- Basic facts like whether they would like to be called by their first name or their surname
- How much sugar they have in their tea, or whether they prefer coffee
- What their insecurities are
- Whether they generally feel cold or warm
- What their interests were before they became ill – this provides material for conversation between the carers and the resident
- A short background, including details of their family, their previous occupation and where they have lived is also useful.

In care homes this information should be easily accessible and kept in an obvious place in the person's room so that everyone knows more about them. It helps to give them an identity in the minds of others at a time when their identity is being eroded.

The Alzheimer's Society has produced a "This is me" tool to help families put their loved one's story together. Sadly, at present, the tool makes no mention of faith or religion.

Normally, volunteers and church workers will be working alongside a family member who either is living with the person with dementia or has a good oversight of the care being provided. It is important for these voluntary helpers to remember that when we help others, the help we offer needs to be wanted and accepted. Be honest and open, and willing to hear feedback about what is not helpful, and also, especially if money is involved, be sure that any money changing hands can be accounted for and that an honest explanation of its use is available. We are bound to get it wrong at times. But we must also remember that people with dementia are vulnerable and are sometimes abused by others. The good done by enormous numbers of faithful Christians should not become obscured by the shocking crimes and scandalous behaviour of a few. Abuse of people with dementia does occur and we must be sure that any such abuse is prevented while we care for those in need.

Activities

But as well as all that, care support includes emotional care and support. Activities can and should be a core component of that support. People with dementia often enjoy trips out, singing, dancing and prayers. Just being able to eat with others may also be both normal and enriching. Music too can be a real help.

In the end, it will be the care we provide by which we are judged. And caring for those in need is central to the Christian faith.

> For I was hungry and you gave me food, I was thirsty and you gave me something to drink, I was a stranger and you welcomed me, I was naked and you gave me clothing, I was sick and you took care of me, I was in prison and you visited me
>
> MATTHEW 25:35 – 6

Carers of people with dementia need support and prayers too. This is discussed in the next chapter.

~ Chapter Eleven ~

Carer support

Carers will tell you that being a carer is one of the hardest things that many people ever do. For all of us, including the most able politicians and bank managers and doctors and nurses and everyone else, being a carer of someone with dementia can be mentally and physically exhausting as well as an enormous organisational challenge. That said, it is absolutely the case that the highest-flying and most organised people are often far from the most able and adept at providing care.

> Carers often find the behaviours of people with dementia very hard to understand and reconcile. It is very important to emphasise to carers that the behaviours are caused by the illness and not the person. That is especially true if carers worry that the behaviours appear sinful.

The reality of providing care is that it requires enormous change and flexibility in the way we do things. It is also often heartbreaking to see a very loved one unwell, distressed and suffering. There is lots of evidence that it is the distress, and the resistance to care, as well as the restlessness, wandering and disinhibition, which carers find most difficult. Sleepless nights, repeatedly getting out of bed and rescuing someone, and just the worry of being unsure if someone is okay all take their toll. The sheer burden of responsibility may be very heavy.

At times we seem to rely upon good fortune. At other times, and especially when someone has gone into care, a real feeling of loss and of having let a loved one down may come to the fore.

Mary got up one night and went out of the front door at about five a.m. Peter was asleep, worn out from the distress of the day before. A few hundred yards up the road, Jean (who was up early for some reason) looked out and saw a lady in slippers and a dressing gown walking up the street. She went out and brought her in, had a cup of tea ready and rang Peter. All was well. Peter made sure in future that the doors were locked at night, with an alarm on the front door.

We usually never know when God has helped us out, but stories like this often seem to be less than chance. While we should never rely upon such a blessing, Peter was convinced that this was truly evidence that he and Mary remained tended by "his love and mercy". It is true that when people with dementia become lost, they may well come to harm, although in my experience, there are so many good people out there that help and a rescue is a far more common outcome than harm.

It is clear that at the right time, a care home is the right place for some people. But that reality does not mean that the loss is easy to cope with. While care at home can be done in the right circumstances and can have excellent results, it is not always possible. Indeed, care at home may be very harmful and distressing for some.

> "Carers need help too. So much of what we do is focused on the person with dementia. But many family carers of people at home also have huge, ongoing and often unmet needs. It is easy for those carers to feel neglected by comparison. I could not have survived as a carer for my mother without very significant practical help and support from my vicar, and without other help from my close friends at church."

There are a lot of resources to help carers, but the work of caring often makes accessing that support difficult. Charities and churches should all be willing to help and support carers of people with dementia. Help with shopping either means buying the shopping or sitting with the person who has dementia while the carer goes out shopping and maybe even for a walk, swimming, or to church. An evening "Granny sitting" while the carer goes out may also help. Just popping round for tea or a glass of wine can be even more helpful.

In fact, many people do not help – not because they are unwilling, but, as a neighbour told one lady after her mother had died, because "we did not know what to do". In many ways that may be understandable as they do not know how to deal with the difficult behaviours and the toileting issues. This problem may well not have an easy solution. It also emphasises that each situation will have its own unique solution. But if a carer can work out some sort of manageable task to share, then they may well find that more people are willing to help and support them. Of all those who want to help, at least some feel unable to do so. With a clear description of what is wanted, however, it may be possible to enable more people to help. Many will then be pleased that they had the chance to give that help.

> It is clear that at the right time, a care home is the right place for some people. But that reality does not mean that the loss is easy to cope with. While care at home can be done in the right circumstances and can have excellent results, it is not always possible. Indeed, care at home may be very harmful and distressing for some.

Yet again, friends, churches and other voluntary and professional people may well have opportunities to help to build a care network around people with dementia. Carers need the help and support of others. Accompaniment is a central theme in good dementia care, and the carers also need to be accompanied.

"Sadly, I found the local Catholic church folk withdrew from my mum when her personality changed. At this time I needed their interest and support more than ever. Perhaps they did not know what to do. Later on in the care home, the church was very supportive. We need to do more to help churches know what to do and how to offer help etc."

"Sometimes just feeling it is OK to ask for help is what is needed. But carers often need courage and struggle to feel able to ask."

- Accompaniment is a central theme in dementia care, and the carers also need to be accompanied.
- Carers are entitled to carer assessment.
- Accessing local voluntary services may also be very helpful.

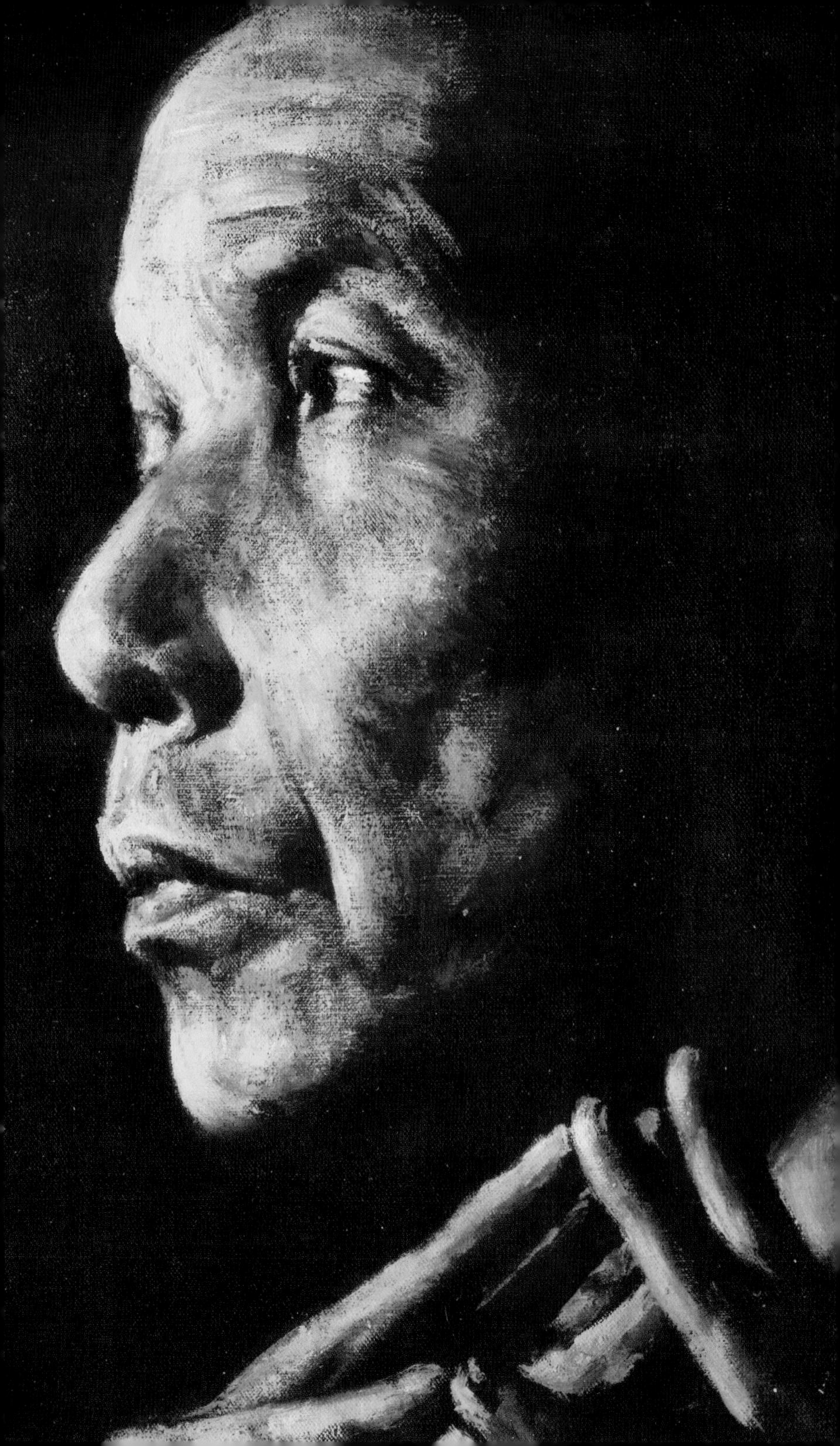

~ Chapter Twelve ~

Emotional care and emotional instability

People with dementia are vulnerable and, at least in some ways, often afraid. The inability to understand what is going on can lead to many complex emotions and much distress. Although some people with dementia do not experience much difficulty in this respect and remain calm and settled and often happy for much of the day and night, others will be fearful and worried, becoming irritable as result.

As well as all that, dementia brings with it a tendency for personalities to sharpen somewhat and also to become less stable. People with dementia may fluctuate from being high, happy and disinhibited, to being very afraid, tearful or aggressive. This emotional instability can be very difficult to cope with and is very stressful for carers.

But in all these circumstances, emotional care and comfort is very important. Enabling people with dementia to feel that somehow they are listened to is important. Answering questions asked repeatedly is also important, even though at the fiftieth time of answering there can be a desperate desire to find a new answer to the same old question! Just comforting and nurturing through the distress felt by a person with dementia is very important.

Distracting people and offering a different avenue of discussion may help. "When in doubt, brew-up" was a wartime slogan, and it can be useful advice in these circumstances also. Doing something else, going somewhere, or just sitting down to a cup of tea may be truly helpful.

Understanding behaviours and understanding the emotions of people

Just getting inside someone's thoughts and ways of understanding things may be the key to dealing with difficult situations. Plumbers and electricians with dementia present special sets of problems. With a screwdriver or spanner, their home can become a workplace. A plumber with dementia can do a great deal of damage in a few minutes! Former head teachers with dementia may forget that they are not at school and try to sort a few things out – and have been known to discipline (usually verbally and with great skill) some carers and workers whom they happen to think are their pupils. Such behaviours are much easier to cope with and manage if they are understood. When the man telling you off is just a man telling you off it may be hard to deal with. When you know he is a former headmaster, you might even be able to admire the skills, now briefly demonstrated, which were honed over decades in classrooms, but which are now obscured by dementia.

Recognising that difficult behaviour is the illness and not the person can be a great help.

As a general rule of thumb, if you can understand why someone is afraid, why they are distressed, you may well find things go a lot more smoothly in your interaction with them.

"Tea break, Sid!"

Before he had dementia, Sid had been a roofer. One afternoon while out in the garden he managed to get onto the roof. Seeing a loose tile, he decided to sort it out. And soon enough tiles were all over the place and falling from the roof. Sid was encouraged to come down, but nothing would move him until he had sorted it all out. There seemed little hope.

Understanding Sid rather better than the others, the nurse came out with cup of tea in hand and shouted up, "Tea break, Sid!" He was quickly down and safe, enjoying his tea.

~ Chapter Thirteen ~

Distress in dementia

The ability to manage and treat distress in dementia is central to good care. Carers find distress and agitation among the most difficult things to cope with. Many will tell you that providing nursing care for someone who has a very advanced dementia and who is immobile is not as difficult as managing those stages of dementia when people are active, restless and very challenging. Lots of research evidence confirms that what are often called "challenging behaviours" in dementia are more stressful than anything else.

When people with dementia are suffering from severe distress they will not always show that distress in the same way each time. Sometimes they may call out or shout, sometimes they may hit out, and sometimes they may just want to walk or go out, or they may search for something. That is often called wandering. At other times they may just withdraw and become silent.

Signs of distress may include things like:

- Anger/frustration
- Aggression/agitation
- Fear/anxiety
- Tearfulness/misery
- Pain when still
- Discomfort on moving
- Restlessness
- Insomnia
- Calling out/vocalisation
- Wandering
- Being aroused, showing signs of sweating, fast pulse

> "One sign of distress was refusal to cooperate. I would then need to gently find out what was wrong."

Whatever the signs of distress are, whatever people with dementia do, and however they react, the most important thing is to try and understand why someone is distressed. Sometimes there may be clues from a person's past, though it is only occasionally the case that we manage to unearth these.

Causes of distress in dementia:

- Depression
- Psychosis
- Medical problems/pain
- Poor understanding
- Fear and anxiety
- Insomnia
- Hunger and diet
- Boredom, isolation and lack of spiritual care
- Poor environment and poor care

Even if the cause of distress does seem obvious it is always worth thinking through the other possible causes of someone's distress. For some it may be pain, while for others it may be depression, and for still others it may be fear. But others too may be hungry, cold or just bored. The list above is useful to help think through the causes of distress. But remember that pain is often missed or undertreated in dementia. Hunger and boredom can also be crucial reasons for distress that are often missed.

The alleviation of distress is centrally important as we strive to make a difficult journey easier. The last thing we want to do is to leave someone suffering who cannot understand why they are suffering. Dementia calls us to care. It calls upon carers to care. But it also calls upon those around the carers to provide care and support as well. Dementia asks a lot of us all. If we cannot support key carers and then also leave the person with dementia unsupported, then that surely is a serious failing?

Pain is often missed or undertreated in dementia.

~ Chapter Fourteen ~

Palliative care of dementia: alleviating distress and promoting comfort

Dementia is a condition that shortens life a lot. On average, people with dementia die just four years after diagnosis. That is less than most cancers. And while the illness itself leads to death, people with dementia who get an infection will usually present for treatment later, they fall more often, and they eat less well, becoming frailer. Weight loss is effectively a normal (though unwanted) part of worsening dementia. Swallowing difficulties and choking all make things worse. As a result, people with dementia die sooner than others. Although the final cause of death is usually something like pneumonia, a stroke, a heart attack, or perhaps a fall, it is without doubt the dementia that lays the foundation for those final illnesses.

> "Many families choose to avoid hospital admissions whenever they can for people with advanced dementia. They are too distressing and may achieve very little. Some admissions are harmful."

That means that dementia is in many ways like advanced and terminal cancer. In advanced illness the aim is to move towards palliation (reducing distress, increasing comfort and managing disabling symptoms). Palliative care moves away from curative and burdensome treatments. In advanced dementia, therefore, a more palliative approach to care , alleviating pain and providing the best possible support and comfort is maybe just what is needed. Indeed, as people with dementia die, it is absolutely right that they are not put through difficult and burdensome treatments which have little or no chance of real benefit. As dementia progresses and the person's condition deteriorates, the benefit of being admitted to an acute hospital dwindles and the distress and harm done by such an admission increases. Acute hospitals, with their noise, buzz and model of care, can become quite toxic places for someone who is very confused, who cannot understand why treatment is needed or given and who is away from home and alone.

"When Mum could no longer enjoy conversation, we played music from her past for her. She loved the old cockney songs and would sit in her bed and sway to the music or clap, enjoying it immensely. She also loved the peace of Gregorian Chant. She managed to recite the words of songs and the words of prayers, even when she was struggling to speak in conversation."

For those who are dying, we know that we will not cure them. Indeed, to offer the hope of a cure to a person dying of cancer is dishonest. But good medicine and good palliative care still offer real help to those who are dying.

By providing symptom relief, by enabling people to come to terms with their illness, and of course through prayer and sacraments, people can become more whole.

Those administering good palliative care should:

- Cherish and value life
- Accept natural death
- See that distress reduction is key
- Be willing to limit care to that which is not burdensome
- Talk to and discuss the situation with relatives

And remember that palliative care can provide excellent results.

Treatment withdrawal and avoiding burdensome treatments

Limiting care is often a right and proper part of good care for someone who is dying of dementia. Continue treatments which are helpful – it is important to remember that care of the dying does not mean giving no treatment. Nor does it mean no fluids. But it does mean avoiding treatments that will not work, or which are painful and distressing. Doctors and nurses need to be willing to be explicit with carers as to the ceiling of treatment and expectations. And any treatment should be based upon a person's needs and not on their prognosis.

> "At the end we did not want hospital care – she came out worse and we would not want her to go there again."

What is palliative care?

Palliative care is named after the pallium which is worn by bishops and, of course, by the Pope. A pallium is defined "as a cloak thrown over something to hide faults". When a bishop puts on his pallium (which carries the image of the cross), he covers his own personal life and becomes a significant representative of Christ. Palliative care accepts the inevitability of death and aims to cloak the symptoms, enabling a person to live as well as possible until they die. And it gives time for their spiritual needs to be thought about.

The ideas behind palliative care and the provision of comfort to those who are dying fit firmly within biblical and Christian teaching. Withdrawal of inappropriate treatment also fits firmly within that teaching. On the other hand, deliberately ending a life is clearly not allowed. The deliberate withdrawal of simply administered fluids with the result that someone dies of dehydration and starvation is also not allowed. But at the very end of life, if someone simply cannot swallow without choking, not giving fluids may be both reasonable and compassionate. In very difficult situations, it may be helpful to get advice from a specialist who understands the biblical and Catholic position on good care of the dying.

> At critical moments in a person's illness, advice from a specialist (or a priest) who understands the biblical and Catholic position on good care of the dying may be very helpful.

The hospice movement has done a lot to set out what good care of those who are dying should be about and what it should look like. Founded in a deep and profound respect for each individual, hospice care should be person centred and aim to alleviate symptoms, while cherishing life and accepting natural death. That is very much a model for more advanced dementia care. It is very good that the hospice movement is increasingly recognising its role in helping people with dementia and their carers/families. But most care of people who are dying with dementia will be provided outside of hospices. The principles of care should be the same whether or not someone is in a hospice.

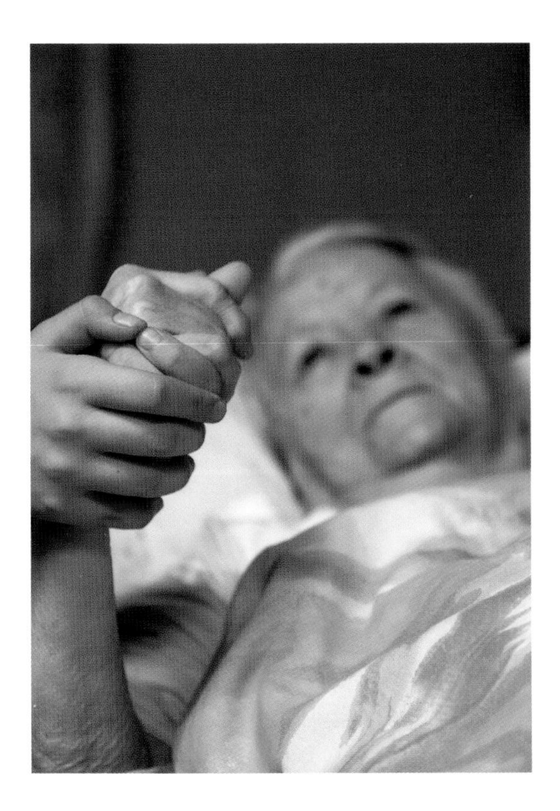

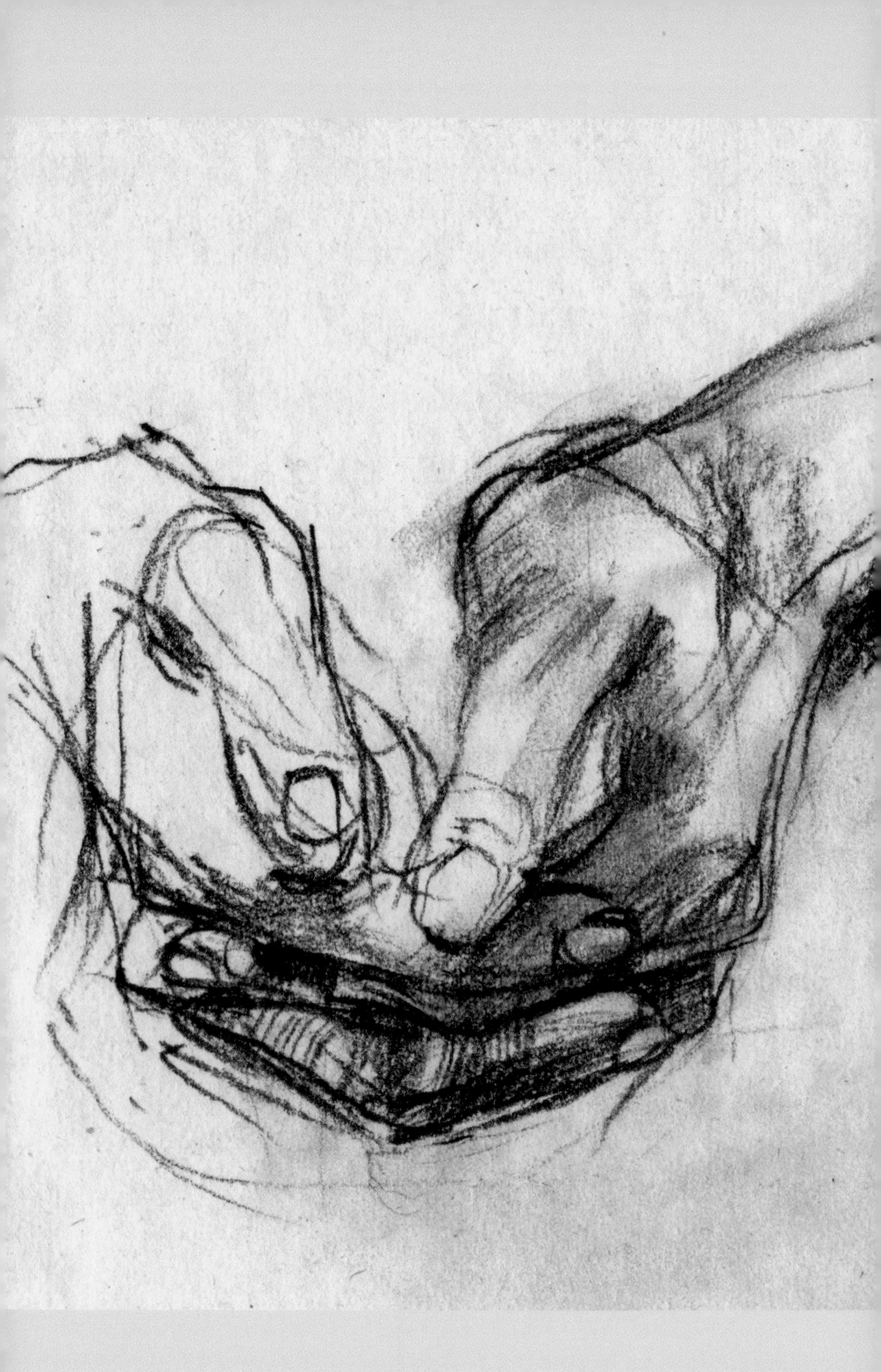

~ Chapter Fifteen ~

Dementia and sin

I have already described how people with dementia may do some pretty awful things. From being ghastly to spouses and family, emotional attacks and insults through to violence, these behaviours may be very hard to bear. As well as that, the person with dementia may well retain the ability to make those attacks as effective as possible. Recognising these behaviours as the illness and not the person can be a great help.

It is true that one of the things that dementia often diminishes is the person's sense of guilt. Guilt is a very useful thing at times. It helps us to know when we ought to restrain ourselves a little. With the loss of guilt, an excellent parent who refined their skills of disciplining their children over many years may become very verbally abusive to the very people who seek to help them. Especially for children and spouses, this can be hugely distressing. They remember and are still affected by the authority of that person, but now that authority is meted out in an irrational and uncontrolled way. With the loss of guilt can come the devastating ability to wreak emotional havoc on a close family member.

Alongside the many examples of good things that people with dementia sometimes do, at times they also do some pretty awful things. Perfectly decent kind and saintly people may start hitting, spitting, swearing and stripping off. I have had wonderfully good Catholics addressing me in very colourful language. These are almost certainly not sins. They are not wilful acts but the result of disordered minds, and we may console ourselves and their families with the thought that they are done in the innocence of dementia. Indeed, in the circumstances, people with dementia are probably just as innocent as a one-year-old.

Examples of such behaviours include shouting, aggression, biting and some very challenging sexual disinhibition. Some may expose themselves or swear like troopers. Sometimes such things are done in great innocence. A man may, for example, mistake another old woman for his wife and then seek to take her to bed. Others may be paranoid and genuinely fear that the person offering them care is about to harm them. Still others may just be disinhibited as a result of the illness they have.

Can people with dementia sin?

According to the Catechism of the Catholic Church, "Sin is an offence against reason, truth, and right conscience; it is failure in genuine love for God and neighbour… It wounds the nature of man and injures human solidarity." But it also states: "Unintentional ignorance can diminish or even remove the imputability of a grave offence." We also know that the Church states that before the age of reason (usually held to be at about six-seven years old), children live in an age of innocence.

What that tells us about dementia is that to commit serious and grave sins requires awareness, understanding and determination. Although the things they do may well be serious actions which may even harm others, we do not think that those actions can be regarded as sins. They are certainly in no way the same as the sins which those of us who have our full faculties commit intentionally and with understanding. By the time a dementia is severe, people have lost the ability to sin. They have gone beyond the age at which they had reason. That is a powerful reason why we should not judge their behaviours. We merely seek to deflect and contain their behaviours so that we minimise the harm they can do.

To commit serious and grave sins requires awareness, understanding and determination. People with dementia often lack that understanding.

~ Chapter Sixteen ~

Despair

We often hope and think that if we embrace hardship, some good will come as a result. God protects and supports those who are his own and who do his work. While that is true, we also know that the rewards for which we hope are either in heaven or often not given "in your face". God works in subtle ways and around the edges. But we all in our lives go through hardship for a greater good later on. A simple example of that is studying for exams, or setting up a business. In each setting we hope for something greater as a result of hardship or sacrifice now. That model also works in dementia care. If we give, and support our loved one, we may well see that care is better, and (sometimes) that our family becomes closer. As well as that, we may sometimes be able to see that the person cared for is happier.

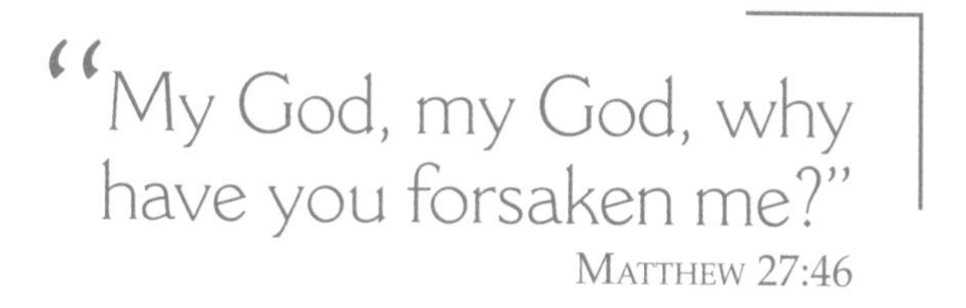

At such times when people are struggling, these words from Psalm 42 might apply: "Why are you cast down, O my soul, and why are you disquieted within me?" But it is unquestionably the case that during the greatest hardships we often lose sight of that hope. Jeremiah wrote during his despair: "O Lord, you have enticed me, and I was enticed; you have overpowered me, and you have prevailed. I have become a laughing-stock all day long; everyone mocks me." And Our Lord even cried out upon the cross: "My God, my God, why have you forsaken me?" At that moment Our Lord without doubt knew that he was fulfilling the prophecies of Psalm 22. In that context there has been much discussion over the centuries about the extent to which Christ felt forsaken and despaired. But it is also absolutely clear that he felt the deepest anguish. His suffering was mitigated only a little by the presence of his Blessed Mother and of those who (like us at times of grave illness) also accompanied him through their suffering and sacrifice.

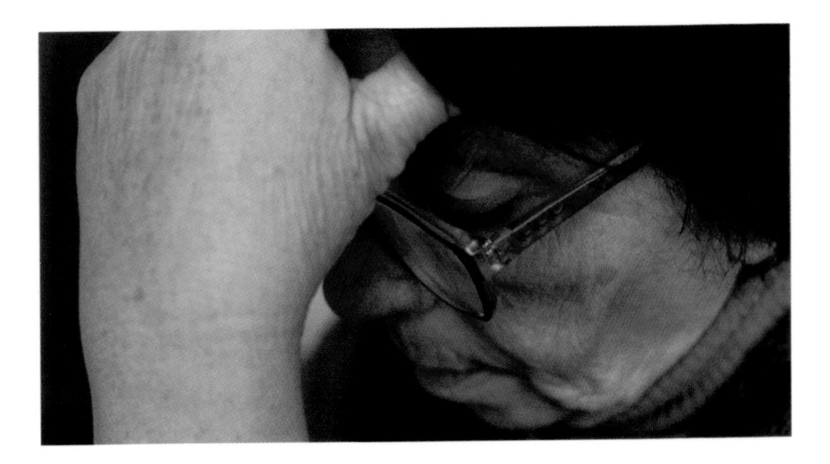

In the depths of a difficult journey, many people with dementia will despair and their carers will find themselves unable to see what good they are doing or what they are achieving. That despair is not failure. It is merely a consequence of how hard the journey can be. St John of the Cross and St Teresa of Ávila both described the "dark night of the soul" – a time when they could no longer see the love of their loving saviour and when they would easily despair.

In the depths of a difficult journey, many people with dementia will despair and their carers will find themselves unable to see what good they are doing or what they are achieving. That despair is not failure. It is merely a consequence of how hard the journey can be.

It is easy to see that at times (especially perhaps when the person with dementia is particularly distressed or challenging) carers will despair. In many ways that is not a sign of weakness. It merely reflects their strength in getting thus far. At such times, we need all the help and support we can get. It may also help us if we can remember the final reward we are promised. In the story of the Holy Innocents, Jeremiah tells us of the women who despaired when Herod killed all their tiny children:

"Thus says the Lord: A voice is heard in Ramah, lamentation and bitter weeping. Rachel is weeping for her children; she refuses to be comforted for her children, because they are no more. Thus says the Lord: Keep your voice from weeping, and your eyes from tears; for there is a reward for your work, says the Lord: they shall come back from the land of the enemy; there is hope for your future, says the Lord: your children shall come back to their own country" (Jeremiah 31:15–17).

If, as a carer, you have symptoms such as not sleeping well, eating poorly and struggling to concentrate, and are feeling very low, unconfident or tearful, remember that depression is common for carers too. Antidepressants can make a huge difference to those who have a depressive illness. Depression is a serious illness that responds to antidepressant medication, and it is important not to miss the chance of treating it.

Despair can be and often is overwhelming. In a dark and difficult tunnel, you may well find it impossible to see the light at the other end. But Jeremiah tells us there truly is hope. God is telling us that your loved one will return to their homeland.

For those of no faith, they also often find hope in seeing that the best care is given, in showing a person the love and respect that they deserve, and also in the memory and the reality of knowing that they did everything possible for that person.

Jeremiah tells us that there truly is hope. God is telling us that your loved one will return to their homeland.

~ Chapter Seventeen ~

Hope

Just as despair can be all-encompassing, so hope brings with it huge comfort and opportunity. As humans, we can have hope in many things, including a good death, going to heaven, and also just being cared for, loved and supported. Much of the care and support that people give bring hope both to patient and carer alike.

> Good advice, encouragement and support from competent professionals and others also bring great hope to patients and carers.

As well as that, seeing families caring for and supporting their loved ones with dementia brings real hope to the staff whose work it is to provide care.

That hope is clearly brought about in part by having the best medical care and social support. But it is also brought about by good spiritual care and prayer.

~ Chapter Eighteen ~

Spiritual care of dementia

Dementia is often seen as a medical illness. But it is much more than that. Most of all, dementia is in fact a social and a spiritual illness; it is, for everyone, about a profound change in life and also part of a journey towards God. So if we neglect the spiritual dimension, then we fail our patients and loved ones.

In fact, health services frequently forget the spiritual aspect and will very often only send for the church at the last moment, if at all. They fail to see the social and spiritual realities of illness. While we focus often upon the medical issues, dementia brings about a profound change in all aspects of life. As mentioned above, dementia is also unquestionably about the final journey of individual sufferers towards God. So if we neglect the spiritual, we fail people with dementia.

Worse still, priests and church visitors are often excluded from the confidential network of hospitals. Church workers are therefore never told there are Catholics or non-Catholic Christians in hospital: the patients must tell us themselves. People with dementia cannot do this, and nor can other very sick individuals. It is really important therefore that churches are informed when these people go into hospital and when they go into care so that the right input and right support for them can be provided there. It is a real tragedy when the sick and vulnerable members of our society are denied access to the spiritual care that they should have a right to receive because of a lack of information about them.

Dementia also brings the opportunity to think and pray about these changes. Given that someone with dementia is no longer as able to practise their faith by themselves, it is really important that we provide them with the opportunity to do so by other means. By doing so we will help to value and respect them as we should. If we leave them alone, we neglect our Christian duty.

She stilled and became calm at the moment of Holy Communion.

Two of the old ladies on the dementia ward in a long-stay hospital were Catholic. So one weekend we thought that they might like the opportunity to go to the hospital Mass. Jean was still able to take part in the Mass. She did so with some effort and some lapses in concentration. Ethel, who had a very severe dementia, sat in her wheelchair and chatted all the way through Mass. But at Communion she stilled and became calm and serene, seeming to pray for a while. We all looked on and marvelled a little. Yes, she recognised Jesus, she saw him, and she knew him.

Those brief moments when it is clear that someone with dementia recognises and understands more than we thought they did are uncommon, but they can be very beautiful and special.

Prayer is a central part of our lifelong relationship with God as well as of our understanding of ourselves. Of course, we usually think that our "faculties" and mental abilities are at the very core of what it is to be ourselves. And being able to see and recognise the eternal and the reality of our creation is an important gift at all stages in life.

Some people find themselves unable to go to church for decades at a time, perhaps due to some impediment, or even because of an interfering mother-in-law or other relative. Others just stop going and forget. And some simply find themselves unable to see the signs of the Creator in the world around them.

Whatever their background, almost all humans naturally seek meaning and hope. And that lifelong search and yearning means that almost everyone with dementia has a spiritual background which they bring with them to the illness.

But one of the mysteries of us as people is the extent to which our eternal soul and spirit is one and the same as our mental faculties. We often think it is, while in fact we recognise that tiny children and those with learning difficulties are no less human than the most able president or world leader. And while we see that those who are disabled have unique gifts and charisma, bringing real change and love to those around them, we still struggle to grasp what we are without our faculties.

Clearly we do not know what we will be like in heaven (or hell), but we are confident that those who have died (as well as God) can hear our prayers, and we have good evidence that those prayers are often answered. Therefore, we think that in heaven, we will have our faculties in at least some form, while at last seeing the glory and joy of the Resurrection. But we also then feel confident that our human soul consists of more than just thought processes and ability. The precise nature of it all remains a mystery. With confidence we predict that it will remain a mystery!

As dementia strips us of our intellectual abilities, therefore, we think in part that humanity is compromised. And yet we also see accentuated into stark relief the gifts that come with that disability. Sometimes, as we have said, people with dementia are happier than they were before they had it. Very often we see that Grandma or Grandad remains just as real to the little ones until the day they die. To some degree, therefore, dementia can help us to see that we are more than the abilities we have. Even in severe disability we are fully human and able to give to those around us. And when finally people with dementia have died, there is still a great emptiness in the house and hearts of those left behind.

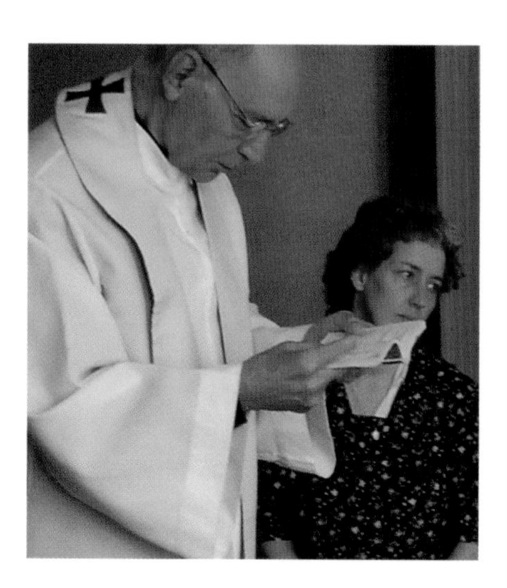

Grandma came to stay, and gave us so much

With cancer and severe dementia, Grandma was doing badly in a home. She and Grandad came home to stay while she died. She had been very distressed and challenging, but as she got worse she settled somewhat, needing full care support and feeding, etc. Soon she was bedbound. Her pregnant daughter became critically ill and had to go to hospital, leaving her son-in-law and the rest of the children at home. As things progressed it became clear that the baby would die soon after birth. But somehow, Grandma, strengthened by the sacraments of the Church, hung on till after the baby had been born and died.

And in the middle of all that, her son-in-law (still doing the full-time day job) realised that even in her extreme illness, she was somehow helping to keep her whole family going. And for the children, Grandma was there, a gift and a real asset at a time of crisis.

It is a fundamental claim of person-centred dementia care that people with dementia continue to have "agency" – which means that they have worth and continue to give to those around them. They have that worth even in the most severe inability. Grandma gave so much, even at the end.

Simple questions you might use to ask about someone's faith background:

- Can you tell me what is your (or your relative's) faith or belief?
- Do you consider yourself/him/her to be spiritual or religious?
- What things do you believe in that give meaning to your life?
- How would you like me and/or your healthcare provider to help you address these issues?

~ Chapter Nineteen ~

Finding out about people's faith background

It is important to try to find out about people's faith background. People should be supported in continuing to practise their lifelong beliefs during an illness such as dementia. As they lose the mental capacity (ability) to ask for spiritual care themselves, UK law states that people around them should act in the "best interests" of the person with dementia. The Mental Capacity Act requires that the person looking after someone who lacks mental capacity should consider "the person's past and present wishes and feelings and the beliefs and values that would be likely to influence his decision if he had capacity".

That places a duty upon decision-makers to think about people's "past wishes and beliefs". It is therefore right and proper to ask people about their past beliefs, wishes and faith background.

These simple questions will usually give an opportunity to discuss things more thoroughly. Often enough people prefer to avoid "the vicar" until nearing the end. That is often to avoid upset. In fact, however, most people report that prayers and the Anointing of the Sick can be very helpful and comforting. It is also reported by many that often some physical improvement is observed afterwards as well.

~ Chapter Twenty ~

Prayer – simple and complex, long and short

Short and simple can be right and good

Usually, when we try to pray with people with dementia we try to do things fairly quickly and unobtrusively. Extraordinary ministers who take Communion to the sick in hospital know this technique well. Especially in hospitals, it is often essential to be quick. With so much going on, and the need to bring the Body of Our Blessed Lord to so many people before the lunch trolley arrives, speed is required.

In my experience, during periods of severe illness, the brief Communion service can be over so quickly that you barely notice it has happened. This is especially so if you are poorly following an operation and drowsy or a bit muddled. In a way it's somewhat like being at Sunday Mass. Many of us struggle to concentrate at Mass, but to reap the graces and gains of Mass we need to be there and to be still for long enough. If the whole thing is over in five minutes we will barely have started to open our hearts to God.

It is the same in many ways for people with dementia. It takes time to still and time to settle into prayer. At first, the person may be restless, they may be thinking of other things. Or they may just be beginning to think about God. Or not. But what we can be relatively confident of is that if they are to feel his presence, that will take a bit of time. So praying with people with dementia is very much like praying with people at other stages of life.

"We carried on saying Grace before eating. She had always done this and it seemed to help make her ready to eat."

Some short prayers are good. Grace before meals, maybe the Angelus or another brief prayer, may help. And think about the odd Our Father, Hail Mary, or short scripture reading. Little and often may well help.

And if the person does not want to know, don't impose it.

Ideas for short prayers

- Our Father
- Hail Mary
- O Sacrament Most Holy
- A brief scripture reading
- Grace before meals
- A few words said together asking for the help of Our Lord or thanking him for what we have
- Some longer scripture readings if you like
- If things are really difficult, the three o'clock prayer for divine mercy

Three o'clock prayer for divine mercy

If you are really struggling, you might try this. Set the alarm on your watch or phone for three p.m. Offer a tiny prayer at three p.m. each day for the mercy of the crucified saviour. Many have found this prayer very helpful in times of crisis.

You expired, O Jesus, but the source of life gushed forth for souls and an ocean of mercy opened up for the whole world. O Fount of Life, unfathomable divine mercy, envelop the whole world and empty yourself out upon us. O Blood and Water, which gushed forth from the heart of Jesus as a fount of mercy for us, I trust in you. Amen.

> "Margaret has a hand-held cross too.
> She fingers it frequently."

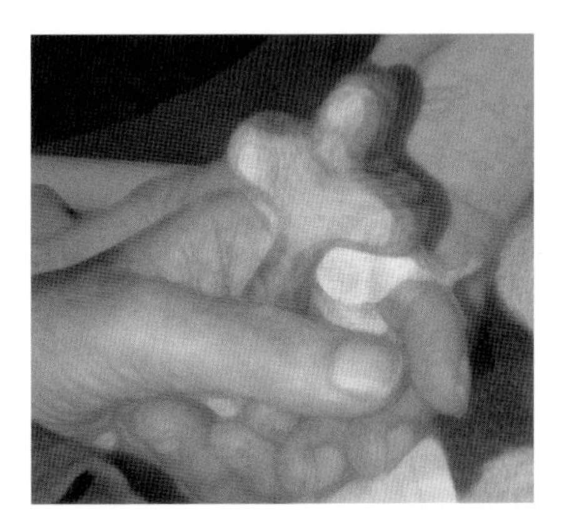

Longer and complex prayer can be better

For most of us, our most prayerful moments will come during episodes of prayer lasting between ten minutes and an hour – which is more like the time it takes to pray the rosary, to pray the daily office, or to be at Mass. In all of these settings, we have longer to wake up to what is going on and to tune our minds in to the needs of others.

Whatever solution you find to be helpful, the prayers may be repeated many times – first, because they are effective prayers to help the sick and dying on their journey to meet Our Lord; and second, because, if they are said aloud in the presence of the person dying, that person will know that those who care about and love them are near.

> "It was important for me to take my mum to Holy Mass for as long as possible, so that she felt the fellowship of the community there. She was included in every week's prayers for the sick. When she could no longer travel physically to the church, the Ministers of the Eucharist would bring her Holy Communion every Sunday morning."

Ideas for longer prayers

- Attend Mass if that is possible
- The rosary
- Divine Office
- Bible readings
- Stations of the Cross
- Prayers for the dying
- A simple little altar with a statue or two near the bed may also be helpful
- There is a special set of prayers for those who are dying or who have just died, taken from the St Andrew Missal

~ Chapter Twenty-one ~

Late illness awareness

People who are dying may often seem to be unconscious or semi-responsive. But we know that often enough there is good awareness and that, even though there may be no response, they will participate in prayers and listen.

"Grandma was dying of advanced dementia at home with her family. She had been unresponsive and had eaten, drunk and said nothing all day. Come the evening, the family gathered around her bed and prayed the Rosary. She made no response at all, until the Fourth Mystery (about 15 minutes in), when she made a sign of the Cross. It was the last purposeful act she ever did. She died that night."

Even when they appear unconscious, we know that people are often aware. It's just that they are not able to let you know. So time, just being close to them, chatting and praying can be central to good-quality care.

We should not forget that there is plenty of evidence that prayer works. Even the doubters are unable to say that prayer does not work. So it is right that at times we pray with the sick, and we need to be able to help some people to pray and to guide them towards prayers that fit the needs that they have.

Take time, be present, and be still. Hold their hand. If you think they do not know you are there, just chat or pray as if they are aware. They are often more aware than you know.

Of course, if prayer works (which we believe it does), prayer does more than just comfort or make us feel good. It can make a real difference and lead to real changes for individuals.

But all of that needs to be done well, gently and sensitively. As fellow Christians, we are called to help people to continue the faith they have practised in life, and to support them in their ongoing journey towards eternity.

With some prayers (such as the Anointing of the Sick [the last rites]), the patient does not need to be conscious or awake. But with other prayers, some awareness is required. Whatever we do, we aim to help others in the way that is right for them.

"When I was younger we had a chaplain on call. We had an unconscious man and he was there, with the patient, providing the spiritual input. We don't see that any more, which is really sad. It was helpful for families too."

~ Chapter Twenty-two ~

Supporting the faith of earlier life – not the time for conversion!

We should aim to support people with dementia in the faith to which they had allegiance before they were poorly. As Blessed Teresa of Calcutta once said, her aim was "to make Catholics better Catholics, Hindus better Hindus and Muslims better Muslims". Once someone has dementia, we do not hope for conversion, but we assist with prayer, practical care and support. We assist where that person is spiritually and support them. But we do not impose or push.

For atheists, we will still seek to provide that care and support, and to show the sort of Christian compassion and kindness which we hope they may recognise at the gates of heaven which they do not expect to see. We are not called to lean upon vulnerable people to convert to our faith and leave their roots. We can support but we must not impose.

When I Survey the Wondrous Cross: Good Friday with the Lord

Margaret, a lifelong Salvation Army officer and missionary, had reached the point where she showed no recognition or awareness of her family. They took her out from her nursing home for the afternoon and she sat, unresponsive, in her wheelchair during the three p.m. service that they were attending with her.

At the end, as the congregation sang, she joined in and mouthed the words:

> When I survey the wondrous cross
> On which the Prince of glory died,
> My richest gain I count but loss,
> And pour contempt on all my pride.
>
> …
>
> Were the whole realm of nature mine,
> That were a present far too small;
> Love so amazing, so divine,
> Demands my soul, my life, my all.

It is not hard to see why such moments give great consolation to those who care for people like Margaret. Margaret was truly there, praying and praising.

Therefore, if we are to pray with people, we should make sure that that is wanted and welcomed by the person with dementia (or their family if they are unable to express agreement). We would not pray with them unless there is a clear suggestion that that is wanted.

On the other hand, we can pray to God for anyone whom we care for or about. Prayer is a conversation with God, and we are therefore free to have that conversation whenever we wish to or feel we should.

We can always pray for atheists or anyone else as a part of our private conversation with God. But we would not expect to share the fact that we have done so with them unless gentle and tactful exploration has indicated that they would welcome that conversation.

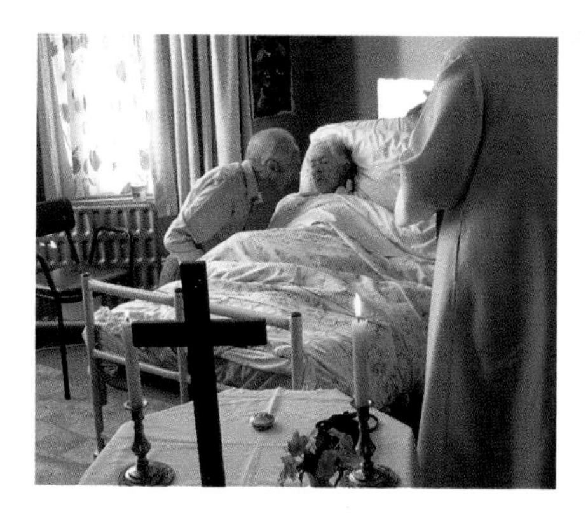

~ Chapter Twenty-three ~

The sacraments

Sacraments are a special way in which graces are obtained from God to help us on our spiritual journey towards heaven. The Catholic Church has seven sacraments, including baptism, marriage and holy orders. Marriage and holy orders require consent, good understanding and discernment and so are rarely even possible in people with dementia. Baptism is something that will almost always have been done before a person gets dementia, and again, it would not be done at that stage unless the person specifically wants it. But it is a good example of what a sacrament is. The pouring of water onto the head, with a set prayer, removes original sin from the baptised person and procures in that person the first graces from God on their journey to heaven.

Sacraments are therefore a concrete means of grace. They procure real graces from God for a person on their journey towards heaven. They are acts done in a special way to enable that grace. For those who suffer, we will most commonly offer Holy Communion, confession and the anointing of the sick. While many see the sacraments as rituals that can (and do) provide comfort for both the afflicted and their carers, they are of course real means of obtaining actual concrete grace, and they must not be neglected or denied to the sick.

Catholics believe that in baptism we are born to Christ, and that in Holy Communion we truly receive the body of Christ. In confession, provided we are repentant, our sins are forgiven by Christ.

In the anointing of the sick we are given the strength, peace and courage to overcome the difficulties that go with serious illness or the frailty of old age. We are also prepared, in a special and spiritual way, to meet Our Lord. Sins are also forgiven by the sacrament of the anointing of the sick.

Through all the sacraments we are helped further along our path of redemption by Christ our Saviour. It is therefore very important that we do what we can to ensure that those who are sick receive the sacraments in the best way that they can. That means families sending for the priest when someone is in hospital and ensuring that the sacraments are still available in a care home or if someone is too ill and frail to get to church.

It should also mean that health and caring services ask about access to spiritual care. Sadly, this is very often forgotten in dementia care, and people of faith often enter their last journey towards heaven without the support of the sacraments. While this may be because health workers do not understand the unique nature of the sacraments, it is also often because they feel embarrassed asking about religion, fearing that they may be criticised or disciplined if they do. Sadly, that deprives many people of real opportunities for prayer and God's grace during their illness.

Try using the simple questions listed on page 106 to start finding out whether someone should be receiving the sacraments or other help.

~ Chapter Twenty-four ~

Confession

Confession does require an awareness of sin, an understanding of repentance, and the ability to articulate both the sins and the repentance. It is by consciously and humbly saying sorry for our sins that we are forgiven. There is a requirement that Catholics should go to confession at least once every year. In confession, "the disclosure or confession of sins to a priest is an essential element of this sacrament. In a profound sense it is also a 'confession' – acknowledgement and praise – of the holiness of God and of his mercy toward sinful man" (Catechism of the Catholic Church [CCC], 1424). The key test of ability to confess sins in dementia is whether or not you can remember and understand what you did and what you are doing in confession. There is no doubt that many people can continue to benefit from the sacrament of confession in early and moderate dementia. But in severe dementia the ability to confess sins is undoubtedly lost.

Therefore confession really ought to be offered as early in the illness as possible. As we have said above, once people have dementia they may do terrible things (e.g. hitting, spitting, swearing, stripping off), but this is all done in the context of illness and therefore almost never sinful. These are not wilful acts but acts of a disordered mind. Just as children below the age of seven are not able to go to confession (because they have yet to reach the age of reason), so people with severe dementia or severe learning difficulties may also be unable to go to confession.

Book early to avoid disappointment!

Offer confession early if you think someone is still able to understand and confess their sins.

But do remember that familiarity will usually increase people's ability to benefit from confession. If a person with mild dementia can get to church, then being able to go into a confessional may make it easier for them to "click" into being in confession mode. With that support they may be able to make a good and valid confession. Others may be afraid or may struggle, and so we would never force anyone to go into a confessional. Others might find that just sitting with the priest and confessing their sins in an open room works best. As ever in dementia care, different people will benefit from different approaches at different times.

> "A prayer that comforted my mother particularly was the Confiteor/'I confess…'. I think it was because she realised that she could not get to confession any more. I would say it out loud and she would say the odd phrase and try to participate, so I know that it was important to her."

~ Chapter Twenty-five ~

Holy Communion

Receiving Holy Communion requires the proper dispositions for doing so. That is, you should be free from serious sin, you should be a baptised Catholic and you should be living in accord with the Church's teaching. For a baptised Catholic with dementia that is not difficult to assume. And if someone is not able to have been recently to confession, they should be able to gain forgiveness of their sins via the anointing of the sick.

More importantly for people with dementia, Holy Communion also requires an understanding and belief that this is something special. It is not necessary to have the full understanding that the Host is truly the body of Christ, although this is, of course, desirable and hoped for in communicants who do not have dementia. In the case of someone with learning difficulties it would only be necessary to establish that they knew the difference between the Eucharist and ordinary bread – "a belief that it is something special". As a result, it may not be suitable for those with very severe dementia who do not understand what the Sacred Host is. It can also be problematic for people who spit it out.

Generally you should probably assume that if someone is likely to spit out the Sacred Host they are failing to understand what is offered. If you were to ask a person who is a devout Catholic whether they would wish to continue receiving Holy Communion if they reached a point where they unwittingly spat out the Sacred Host, they would surely say that they would not wish to receive it in those circumstances. This is not a question of a person being "unworthy", but rather one of respecting the dignity of someone who has always lived a devout Catholic life.

"I once took a lady to Mass who had a quite severe dementia which caused her quite a lot of distress. She chatted all the way through Mass and looked somewhat distressed. However, at Communion she stilled and became calm. It was not only me who thought that a significant spiritual change came upon her at the time she received Holy Communion."

So the bar to receiving Communion is really quite low, but if you clearly expect that giving it will cause the Host to be spat out, then perhaps it is best to pray and not actually give Communion. If there is doubt, then perhaps a very small fragment of a Sacred Host is a good idea. Our blessed Lord's body is present in equal measure regardless of the size of Host given.

If in the end the Sacred Host is spat out, then you can probably consume it yourself. You may not like doing this, but it is pretty safe to do so and very rare to get any infection as a result. There is no evidence that you could contract dementia by doing this, and

"When my mum could no longer join in with the prayers, and her sight and hearing were failing, I would sit close to her and relay the prayers to her. She always became solemn and prayed quietly after receiving Holy Communion. Her profound faith never wavered, even at the height of her confusion. She often moved the ministers of the Eucharist with her devotion. When the ministers of the Eucharist were noticed by some of the other residents, they too asked to join us in my mum's room for Holy Communion. Their families had not realised how comforting the Holy Eucharist is to those with dementia."

it will protect the Host from further indignity. The alternative (remembering it to be truly the Body of Christ and thus due very special reverence) is to take it back to church and put it in a glass of water beside the tabernacle until it no longer has the form of bread. By then it can be disposed of, and the recommended method for this is to dispose of it into the sacrarium (or directly into the ground if the church does not have a sacrarium). Sacraria are like sinks, but they drain directly into the earth. Because the Host is so precious, disposal should never be down a drain. While to some people such caution may seem daft, it does in fact enable us to show the extreme love and reverence we wish to have for Christ our Saviour.

It is wonderful that so many thousands of extraordinary ministers take Communion to the sick each week. That work brings many benefits, including the sacrament which they administer. Extraordinary ministers can also be a gateway to thinking of other different ways to bring help and support to those in need. The Catholic Church is one of the largest providers of health and social care in the world, doing huge amounts of good work. The well-established system of extraordinary ministers bringing Communion to the sick is something for all Churches to build upon.

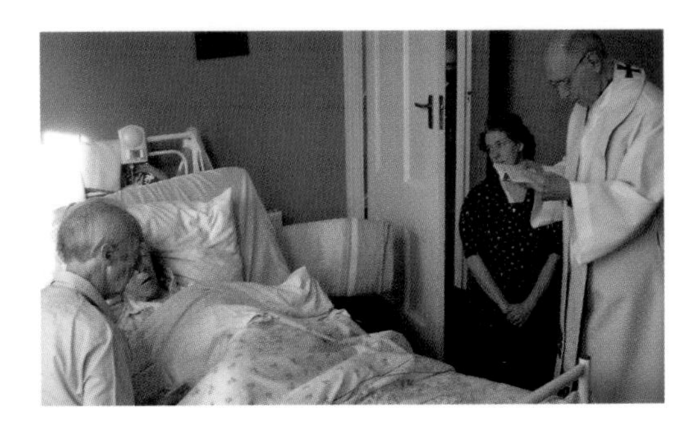

~ Chapter Twenty-six ~

Anointing of the sick (sacrament of the sick or last rites)

The Catechism of the Catholic Church tells us: "By the sacred anointing of the sick and the prayer of the priests the whole Church commends those who are ill to the suffering and glorified Lord, that he may raise them up and save them. And indeed she exhorts them to contribute to the good of the People of God by freely uniting themselves to the Passion and death of Christ" (CCC, 1499).

The sacrament of anointing of the sick (formerly referred to as extreme unction or last rites) is for people with serious or life-threatening illness, including old age. It can be received more than once during the same illness if the patient's condition becomes more serious, or if an elderly person's frailty becomes more pronounced. It is best not to be left to the last minute.

"The Anointing of the Sick is not a sacrament for those only who are at the point of death. Hence, as soon as anyone of the faithful begins to be in danger of death from sickness or old age, the fitting time for him to receive this sacrament has certainly already arrived" (CCC, 1514).

Of especial importance for people with dementia, the anointing of the sick enables forgiveness of sins in those who are no longer able to go to confession. Clearly, it is right that this sacrament should be given to Catholics who have dementia.

It is best if it can be done when someone is conscious, but if someone is seriously unwell and unconscious it should not be delayed in the hope of the person recovering consciousness. Indeed, many have observed that some people who receive this sacrament appear to improve physically and end up surviving when that was not anticipated.

The sacrament brings with it several graces, including the forgiveness of sins, and with the anointing, it helps to prepare a person for their journey to heaven. Of especial importance for people with dementia, the anointing of the sick enables forgiveness of sins in those who are no longer able to go to confession. Clearly, it is right that this sacrament should be given to Catholics who have dementia.

Preparation for the final journey

The special grace of the sacrament of the anointing of the sick has as its effects:

- The uniting of the sick person to the passion of Christ, for his own good and that of the whole Church
- The strengthening, peace and courage to endure in a Christian manner the sufferings of illness or old age
- The forgiveness of sins, if the sick person was not able to obtain it through the sacrament of penance
- The restoration of health, if it is conducive to the salvation of his soul
- The preparation for passing over to eternal life (CCC 1532)

"Mum was anointed more than once. I would call the priest whenever she went into a dip health-wise and I know that this would have comforted her enormously. It comforted me too. She was once fast asleep and very ill. I placed my hand gently over her heart and prayed for her. Without opening her eyes, or changing her deep breathing, she clasped my hand and said 'thank you' to me. She knew I was praying for her."

"I would do it all again. Looking after Grace was not hard work. I coped because I was doing something for her. I had a goal, which was doing something beneficial to her – I could manage. As long as I was able to do what she would have loved, I didn't have time to mourn."

~ Chapter Twenty-seven ~

Bereavement and beyond

As we prepare to say goodbye to our loved ones, many hope that the final goodbye may be easier as a result of the preceding dementia. Some regard the slow loss of memory over the months and years leading up to death as a real part of their bereavement. Others may feel that they had longer to prepare for bereavement as their loved one's deterioration had made it clear that death was approaching for some time. That may well be true, and it is certainly true that having been able to support someone during their final illness can make bereavement easier for those left behind. The opportunity to hope in the person's resurrection with Christ may also help.

But in the end, death is a very clear moment and a very clear "Goodbye". The loss of a loved one with dementia, even at a very advanced age, is still a real wrench and a real loss. Life is still emptier once they have gone. Bereavement takes many forms, and losing a loved one is never easy. But we can hope one day to meet up once more in his heavenly kingdom.

~ Chapter Twenty-eight ~

Conclusion

Dementia can indeed be a difficult journey. Accompanying someone on the journey can also be terribly hard. But it is a journey which requires the care and support of many, including Churches and their faithful. There is much to do. Churches have a duty to support people with dementia and their carers, and they must be sure to deliver on that duty of care and support. The Churches have plenty to learn, for with better understanding of dementia, more can be done. The parable of the Good Samaritan does not get much closer to reality than it does with dementia.

~ Chapter Twenty-nine ~

Resources

The Catholic Church in England and Wales provides information on the Mental Capacity Act and Living Wills (2008): <www.cbcew.org.uk/.../file/mental-capacity-act-and-living-wills-A5.pdf>

Hope for Home is a registered charity set up to support and promote care of people with dementia at home until they die: <www.hopeforhome.org.uk>

Pastoral Care Project – Dementia prayer week.
The Pastoral Care Project provides resources in the form of prayers and support for people with dementia and their families, as well as organising a National Week of Prayer for Dementia each year: <www.pastoralcareproject.org.uk/dementia---prayer-week.html.>

Prayer Resources:
<www.catholicmedicalassociation.org.uk/prayers.htm>